Laboratory Identification

of

Pathogenic Fungi Simplified

Publication Number 370

AMERICAN LECTURE SERIES ®

A Monograph in

The BANNERSTONE DIVISION *of*

AMERICAN LECTURES IN TESTS AND TECHNIQUES

Edited by

GILBERT DALLDORF, M.D.

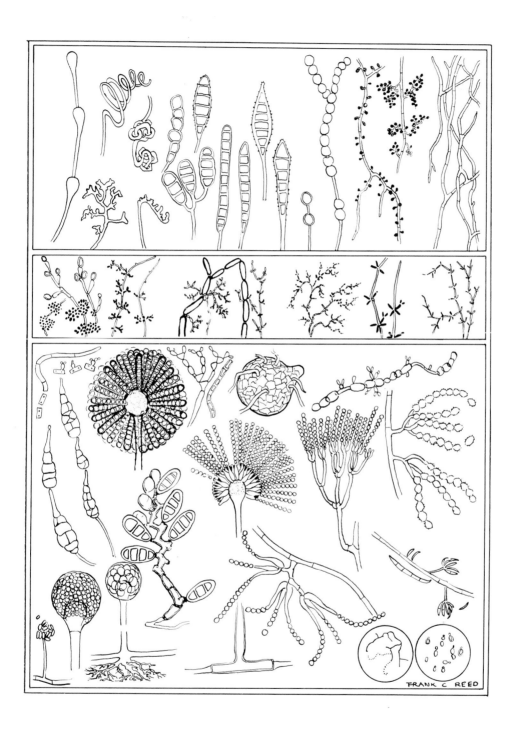

FRANK C REED

(Second Edition)

Laboratory Identification

of

Pathogenic Fungi Simplified

By

ELIZABETH L. HAZEN, Ph.D.
Associate Bacteriologist (Mycology)

and

FRANK CURTIS REED
Laboratory Illustrator and Photographer

Division of Laboratories and Research
New York State Department of Health
Albany, New York

CHARLES C THOMAS • PUBLISHER
Springfield • *Illinois* • *U.S.A.*

CHARLES C THOMAS • PUBLISHER
BANNERSTONE HOUSE
301-327 East Lawrence Avenue, Springfield, Illinois, U.S.A.

Published simultaneously in the British Commonwealth of Nations by
BLACKWELL SCIENTIFIC PUBLICATIONS, LTD., OXFORD, ENGLAND

Published simultaneously in Canada by
THE RYERSON PRESS, TORONTO

Library of Congress Catalog Card Number: 59-14198

With THOMAS BOOKS careful attention is given to all details of manufacturing and design. It is the Publisher's desire to present books that are satisfactory as to their physical qualities and artistic possibilities and appropriate for their particular use. THOMAS BOOKS will be true to those laws of quality that assure a good name and good will.

Printed in the United States of America

Preface to the Second Edition

THE OBJECTIVE of the second edition remains the same as that of the first—an aid in the teaching of the essentials in the identification of pathogenic fungi to the beginner and as a bench companion for the bacteriologist engaged in mycologic diagnosis.

Many additions and substitutions have been made in the hope of increasing the usefulness of the monograph. A section has been added on the contaminants commonly encountered in the laboratory and so often mistaken for pathogenic fungi by the inexperienced. The colonial and microscopic characteristics by which these saprophytic fungi can be identified and differentiated from the pathogen are described and illustrated photographically.

In the section on the pathogenic fungi, incitants of South American blastomycosis, aspergillosis, mucormycosis, and moniliasis incited by species of *Candida* other than *Candida albicans* are described. South American blastomycosis is not endemic in North America but travel between the two continents is so common that the possibility of infection in persons who have been in South America should not be overlooked. The systemic form of aspergillosis and mucormycosis has increased since the advent of the broad spectrum antibiotics, steroids, and folic acid antagonists.

Drawings of characteristic microscopic structures of some of the common fungi constitute a new frontispiece which should be useful to the student in testing his ability to identify these fungi. Some of the photomicrographs have been replaced with better prints. Recent references have been included in the bibliography and new formulae have been added to the list of media.

Again we acknowledge with deep appreciation the valuable assistance of our many colleagues, without which this second edition would not have been possible.

E. L. H.
F. C. R.

Preface to the First Edition

THIS MONOGRAPH is the outgrowth of an experience in teaching diagnostic mycologic methods to students who had been trained in bacteriologic procedures but who had little or no experience in the field of mycology. Some students were assistants in this laboratory; some were visitors from other laboratories; and some were physicians preparing to direct local laboratories in New York State. All wished to become familiar in a short time with the essential procedures and criteria in the identification of the incitants of fungus infections.

As a visual aid in this program of instruction, the exhibit panel shown in the *Frontispiece* was designed to present the characteristic features upon which the identification of the pathogenic fungi is based. Giant living colonies and diagrammatic drawings of the microscopic structures familiarized the students with the morphology of the fungi. The exhibit was also used effectively in lecture-demonstrations to medical students. Later, as a matter of convenience, photographs of the individual sections of the exhibit were bound, with a supplementary text, as a manual for use at the laboratory bench. Impetus to make the manual more widely available came from the response of members of the New York State Association of Public Health Laboratories to whom it was shown at the Annual Meeting in 1952. In the present book photomicrographs replace the drawings of the original exhibit. Tabular and other textual descriptive information has been added, together with formulae of the essential culture media and a selective list of references. The objective remains the same as in the earlier presentations, namely, an aid to the teaching of the essentials in the identification of the pathogenic fungi to the beginner and a bench companion for the bacteriologist engaged in mycologic diagnosis.

Only those pathogenic fungi commonly encountered in North America are included in this work, and all illustrations are from cultures studied in this laboratory. The pathogenic fungi are, with few exceptions, members of the class of Fungi Imperfecti, that is, fungi in which the sexual spore has not been demonstrated. Identification is based upon asexual spores, the conidia, which are borne on specialized hyphae (conidiophores). The diseases caused by the pathogenic fungi have been roughly classified into superficial and systemic or deep-seated mycoses.

In publishing this monograph our appreciation goes to the students whose responses have helped us to sharpen the various presentations. Acknowledgment is also made to our colleagues whose encouragement and valuable assistance are responsible for the decision to offer to others this outline of a practical laboratory experience.

E. L. H.
F. C. R.

Contents

[xiii]

Laboratory Identification

of

Pathogenic Fungi Simplified

Aided by a grant from the Brown-Hazen Fund

Superficial Mycoses

Dermatophytoses (Ringworm)

THE SUPERFICIAL MYCOSES are the most common and widely distributed of all fungus diseases. They are confined to the keratinized layers of skin and its appendages, but nevertheless are of major importance, since they are so widespread and may cause great discomfort and even at times are very disabling.

These diseases are incited by a group of fungi, the dermatophytes, embracing many species. The isolation and identification of the fungus from scrapings from skin lesions, infected nails, or from stubs of broken hairs are essential to specific diagnosis.

This group of fungi is represented by three genera, based upon the type of macroconidia (fuseaux) formed, *Microsporum, Trichophyton,* and *Epidermophyton.*

Note: The dermatophytes are usually easily isolated on Sabouraud's glucose agar at room temperature; however, in cases of grossly contaminated specimens, a selective isolation agar, Mycosel (Baltimore Biological Laboratory, Inc.) should be used.

Microsporum

The genus *Microsporum* consists of three commonly recognized species, *M. audouini*, *M. canis*, and *M. gypseum*. They attack hair and glabrous skin. These fungi are the chief incitants of ringworm of the scalp (tinea capitis) among children in the United States. The infected hair shows a sheath of spores in the form of a mosaic about the hair shaft (ectothrix type), and under filtered ultraviolet light (Wood's lamp) there is a brilliant green fluorescence. In the infected skin, segmented branching mycelium is found.

They form cottony or downy, matted or powdery aerial mycelium, and vary in color from white to grayish-white, or buff to various shades of brown.

They produce characteristic, large, thick, rough or smooth-walled, multiseptate, spindle-shaped macroconidia (fuseaux), and small, single-celled, clavate spores, attached directly or to short sterigmata on the sides of the hyphae; pectinate hyphae, nodular bodies, racquet hyphae, and chlamydospores are also formed.

MICROSPORUM AUDOUINI

Media for Development of Significant Characters

MACROSCOPIC	
Sabouraud's glucose agar.	Flat, grayish-white, velvety, aerial mycelium (with button in center); rose-brown pigment on under-surface.
Polished rice grains.	No aerial mycelium, brownish discoloration of grains.

MICROSCOPIC	
Corn meal agar.	Pectinate hyphae.
Honey agar plus yeast extract (10 mg./ml.).	Macroconidia, microconidia.
Incubated at 25° C.	

MICROSPORUM AUDOUINI

THE SPECIES *Microsporum audouini* is of human origin and is the chief agent of tinea capitis among children in the United States. This dermatophyte also attacks glabrous skin.

Cultural and Microscopic Characteristics

The colony on Sabouraud's glucose agar is slow-growing, flat, with a button in the center and a surface of grayish-white, closely matted, velvety, sometimes fluffy, aerial mycelium, occasionally showing radial foldings; a rose-brown pigment on the under-surface.

Microscopically, large, thick, rough or smooth-walled, multi-septate, spindle-shaped macroconidia (fuseaux) and numerous single-celled, clavate microconidia and pectinate hyphae may be seen. The macroconidia can seldom be demonstrated on Sabouraud's glucose medium. An enriched medium is required.

MICROSPORUM AUDOUINI

Figure 1

A. Colony on Sabouraud's glucose agar after three weeks.

B. Honey agar plus yeast extract slide culture preparation showing multiseptate, spindle-shaped macroconidia and clavate microconidia.
X 400.

C. Culture mount from corn meal agar showing pectinate hyphae.
X 400.

D. Infected hair with small spores, forming sheath around hair. X 400.

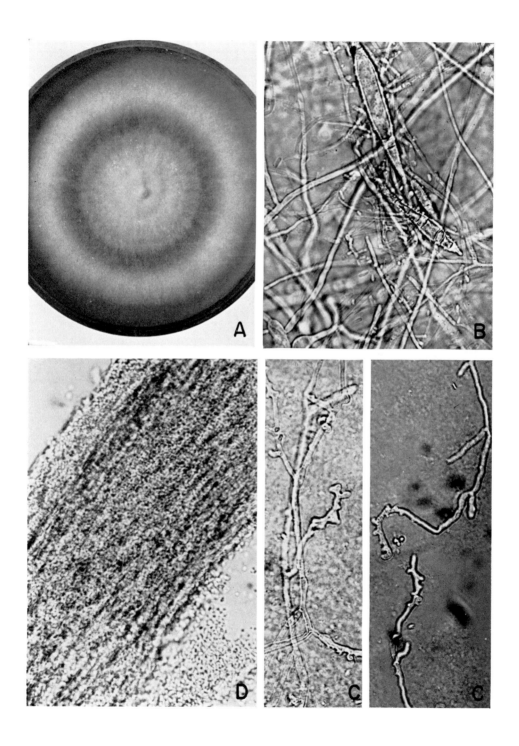

MICROSPORUM CANIS

Media for Development of Significant Characters

MACROSCOPIC	
Sabouraud's glucose agar.	White, cottony or wooly, aerial mycelium, becoming powdery with age; bright yellow to orange pigment on undersurface.
Polished rice grains.	Grains covered with heavy, white, cottony, aerial mycelium, becoming powdery with age; pinkish-buff discoloration of medium.

MICROSCOPIC	
Sabouraud's glucose agar.	Macroconidia, microconidia.
Polished rice grains.	Macroconidia, microconidia.

MICROSPORUM CANIS

(Microsporum lanosum, Microsporum felineum)

THE SPECIES *Microsporum canis* is of animal origin and is responsible for roughly 10 per cent of tinea capitis among children in the United States. This fungus also attacks glabrous skin.

Cultural and Microscropic Characteristics

The colony on Sabouraud's glucose agar develops fairly rapidly, forming a white, cottony or wooly, aerial mycelium, becoming powdery with a central depressed area, sometimes showing radial folds. The pigment on the undersurface is yellowish-orange, later changing to reddish-brown.

Microscopically, numerous large, thick, rough-walled, multiseptate, spindle-shaped macroconidia (fuseaux) and numerous clavate or elongated microconidia are found. Racquet hyphae and chlamydospores are also present.

MICROSPORUM CANIS

Figure 2

A. Colony on Sabouraud's glucose agar after three weeks.

B. Slide culture preparation, stained with lactophenol cotton blue, showing numerous macroconidia and small, single-celled microconidia.
X 600.

C. Multiseptate, spindle-shaped macroconidia. X 400.

D. Young macroconidia attached to hyphal branches. X 400.

E. Racquet hypha. X 400.

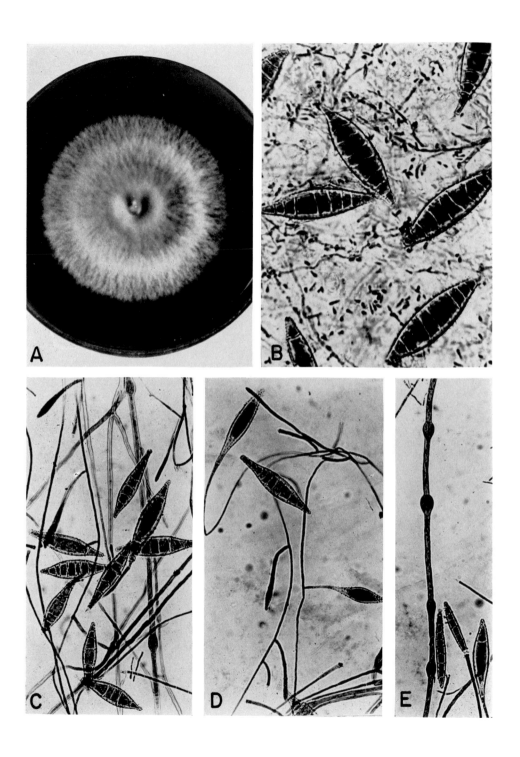

MICROSPORUM GYPSEUM

Media for Development of Significant Characters

MACROSCOPIC	
Sabouraud's glucose agar.	Powdery, aerial mycelium of buff to light brown or cinnamon color.
Polished rice grains.	Grains covered with powdery, aerial mycelium of pinkish-cinnamon color.

MICROSCOPIC	
Sabouraud's glucose agar.	Macroconidia.
Polished rice grains.	Macroconidia.

MICROSPORUM GYPSEUM

(*Microsporum fulvum*)

THE SPECIES *Microsporum gypseum,* long considered to be of animal origin, has more recently been found to be a soil-inhabiting fungus. Of the three microspora, it is least commonly encountered as the cause of tinea capitis or ringworm of the glabrous skin.

Cultural and Microscopic Characteristics

The colony is comparatively fast-growing, shows a central cottony boss, surrounded by a flat, powdery, cinnamon-brown mycelium terminating in a border of downy, white mycelium. The pigment on the undersurface is reddish-brown.

Microscopically, numerous large, rough, thick-walled multi-septate, spindle-shaped macroconidia with slightly rounded ends are found.

MICROSPORUM GYPSEUM

Figure 3

A. Colony on Sabouraud's glucose agar after three weeks.

B. Numerous, large, rough, thick-walled, multiseptate, spindle-shaped macroconidia with blunt ends. X 400.

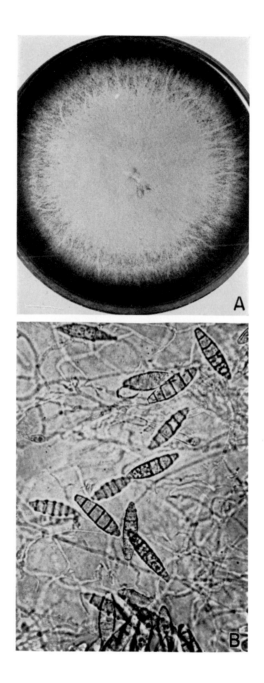

TRICHOPHYTON

THE GENUS *Trichophyton* contains a large number of species which attack glabrous skin, bearded areas, hair, and nails, and causes a wide variety of lesions, depending upon the species and the site of infection. Infected hairs show either chains of spores outside the shaft (ectothrix type) or parallel rows of spores within the shaft (endothrix type).

Cultural and Microscopic Characteristics

These fungi form cottony, velvety, finely granular to powdery, or glabrous aerial mycelium, and vary in color from white to brown, violet to purple, pink to red, or yellow to orange.

The macroconidia (which cannot always be demonstrated in every species) are large, clavate, smooth, thin-walled, multiseptate. The microconidia, produced in abundance in some species, are single-celled and are globular, clavate or pyriform in shape, and may be borne singly along the sides of the hyphae (en thyrse) or in grape-like clusters (en grappe). Other structures which may be produced are spiraled hyphae, nodular bodies, racquet mycelium, and chlamydospores. Typical of some species of *Trichophyton* is the formation of the knobbed hyphal structures called "favic chandeliers" as their only identifying characters.

TRICHOPHYTON MENTAGROPHYTES

Media for Development of Significant Characters

MACROSCOPIC

Sabouraud's glucose agar.	Downy type—white, velvety to fluffy, aerial mycelium, light buff to tan to brown on reverse surface; granular type—white, powdery to granular, aerial mycelium sometimes pinkish, light buff to yellow to reddish-brown pigment on reverse side. Cottony type—white, fluffy, aerial mycelium, light buff to tan on reverse side.
Corn meal agar plus 1% glucose.	No pigment on undersurface.

MICROSCOPIC

Sabouraud's glucose agar, wort, or corn meal agar.	Microconidia, macroconidia, spirals, nodular bodies.
Cottony type: Sabouraud's glucose agar, wort, or corn meal agar.	Few or no microconidia.

Trichophyton mentagrophytes

(Trichophyton gypseum)

THE SPECIES *Trichophyton mentagrophytes* includes many variants. This dermatophyte is the chief incitant of the inflammatory type of ringworm, involving the feet (athlete's foot), hands, and glabrous skin, particularly of the intertriginous areas. The fungus also attacks nails, bearded areas, and the scalp, causing the ectothrix type of hair.

Cultural and Microscopic Characteristics

The variants of this species on Sabouraud's glucose agar show marked differences in colonial appearance, the colonies having aerial mycelium ranging from cottony to powdery, of white to cream to tan or pinkish color with cream to tan to reddish-brown pigment on the reverse surface.

Microscopically, there are found in the downy and granular types numerous clavate to pyriform microconidia borne singly along the sides of the hyphae (en thyrse) and in clusters (en grappe); typical, long, clavate, thin-walled, multiseptate macroconidia with constriction at septa. Characteristic spiraled hyphae and nodular bodies may also be present. In some of the variants, particularly the fluffy or cottony forms, no identifying structures or only a few microconidia may be found.

Trichophyton mentagrophytes

Figure 4

Growth on Sabouraud's glucose agar after two weeks.

A. Cottony type.

B. Powdery to granular type.

Microscopic structures—powdery type:

C. Stained slide culture preparation, showing microconidia in clusters.
X 600.

D. Typical multiseptate, clavate macroconidia. X 400.

E. Culture mount from corn meal agar, showing nodular bodies. X 400.

F. Spiraled hyphae. X 600.

G. Microconidia along sides of hyphae. X 400.

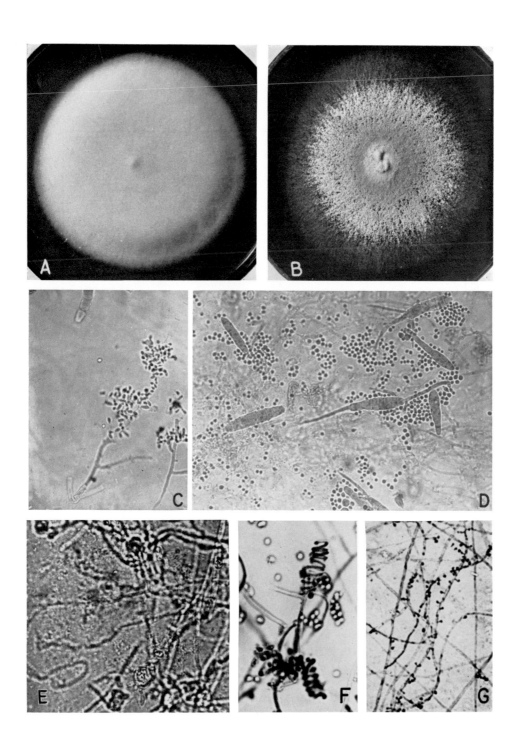

Trichophyton rubrum

Media for Development of Significant Characters

MACROSCOPIC	
Sabouraud's glucose agar.	Cottony mycelium, becoming velvety to powdery with central umbo; reddish-purple pigment on reverse side.
Corn meal plus 1% glucose.	Wine-red pigment on undersurface.

MICROSCOPIC	
Blood agar base (Difco).	Macroconidia, microconidia.

Trichophyton rubrum

(*Trichophyton purpureum*)

THE SPECIES *Trichophyton rubrum* is the commonest incitant of chronic dermatophytosis of the hands and feet, nails, and glabrous skin; the fungus may also involve the bearded areas including the hair follicles.

Cultural and Microscopic Characteristics

The colony on Sabouraud's glucose agar at an early stage is white, fluffy, and hemispheric, later becoming velvety to powdery with a central umbo and sometimes showing radial folds; on the undersurface there is a characteristic reddish-purple pigment.

Microscopically, long, slender, thin-walled, multiseptate macroconidia (fuseaux) with parallel sides and large numbers of pyriform microconidia borne from sides of hyphae are found. For demonstration of the macroconidia a special medium is required.

Trichophyton rubrum

Figure 5

A. Colony on Sabouraud's glucose agar after eight days.

B. Colony after three weeks.

C and D. Blood agar base slide culture preparations, stained with lactophenol cotton blue, showing microconidia along sides of hyphae and long, multiseptate macroconidia. X 400.

E. Direct preparation from skin of patient with ringworm. X 400.

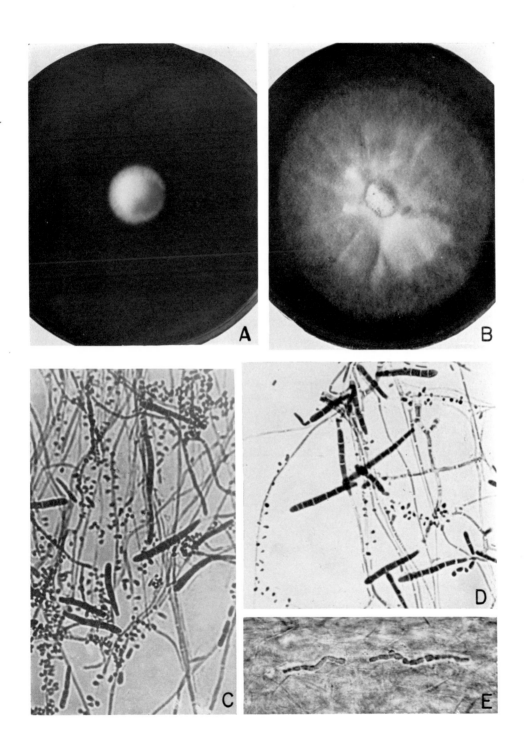

TRICHOPHYTON TONSURANS

Media for Development of Significant Characters

MACROSCOPIC

Sabouraud's glucose agar.	Heaped, irregularly folded, usually finely powdery aerial mycelium, creamy-white to tan to yellow, or shades of rose; on reverse dark-brown pigment.

MICROSCOPIC

Sabouraud's glucose agar.	Microconidia, irregularly branched hyphae, many chlamydospores.
Polished rice grains.	Macroconidia, microconidia.

TRICHOPHYTON TONSURANS

(Trichophyton crateriforme)

THE SPECIES *Trichophyton tonsurans* attacks hair, glabrous skin, and nails. The hairs show the endothrix type of infection.

Cultural and Microscopic Characteristics

The culture is comparatively slow-growing on Sabouraud's glucose agar. The colony is heaped and folded, sometimes showing a central crater or a central prominence, with a surface of compact, velvety or powdery, aerial mycelium of creamy-white, tan, yellow, or shades of rose; the pigment on the undersurface is dark-brown.

Microscopically, there are large numbers of clavate or elongated microconidia attached singly to the sides of the hyphae or in loose clusters, and few thin-walled, club-shaped macroconidia; long, thick, and irregularly branched hyphae and many chlamydospores.

TRICHOPHYTON TONSURANS

Figure 6

A. Colony on Sabouraud's glucose agar after five weeks.

B. Sabouraud's glucose agar slide culture preparation, stained with lactophenol cotton blue, showing microconidia borne laterally on hyphae and in clusters. X 400.

C. Growth from polished rice grains, showing masses of microconidia.
X 600.

D. Growth from polished rice grains, showing thin-walled, clavate macroconidia. X 400.

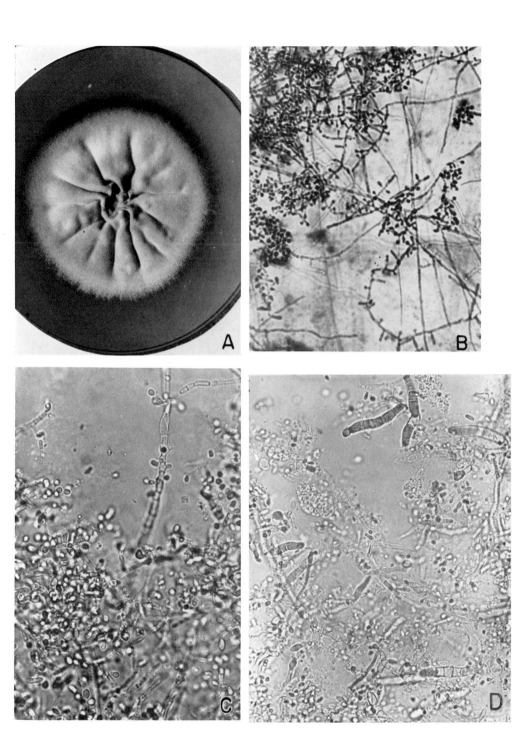

Trichophyton verrucosum

Media for Development of Significant Characters

MACROSCOPIC	
Sabouraud's glucose agar.	Glabrous, heaped-up cerebriform colony; or disc-shaped with white, velvety mycelium; or a much wrinkled glabrous colony of bright yellow color.
Blood agar base plus thiamine.	

MICROSCOPIC	
Blood agar base plus thiamine.	Irregularly branched hyphae, macroconidia, microconidia, chlamydospores.
Polished rice grains.	Macroconidia, microconidia, chlamydospores.

TRICHOPHYTON VERRUCOSUM

(Trichophyton faviforme)

THE SPECIES *Trichophyton verrucosum* includes three varieties: album, discoides, ochraceum. This microorganism causes a suppurative type of ringworm, involving the deeper layers of the skin and the hair follicles. Infected hairs show large spores arranged in chains forming a sheath on the outside of the hairs (ectothrix type) and mycelial elements within the hair shaft. Human infection is acquired directly or indirectly through contact with cattle having ringworm lesions. The fungus may be isolated on Sabouraud's glucose agar, but usually an enriched medium is required.

Cultural and Microscopic Characteristics

The three varieties of *T. verrucosum* differ markedly in colonial appearance, varying from a glabrous, heaped-up, cerebriform, slightly yellowish colony (*T. verrucosum* var. album) to a flat, disc-shaped colony covered with a short, white, aerial mycelium (*T. verrucosum* var. discoides) or a much wrinkled, glabrous, flat colony of a bright yellow color (*T. verrucosum* var. ochraceum).

Microscopically, there will be seen long, multiseptate macroconidia with pointed or bulbous distal ends; elongated, pear-shaped microconidia borne sessile along the sides of the hyphae or in terminal clusters; irregularly branched hyphae with vast numbers of intercalary and terminal chlamydospores. Special media are essential for demonstration of macroconidia.

Trichophyton verrucosum

Figure 7

Colonies on blood agar base plus thiamine.

A. *T. verrucosum* var. discoides after two weeks.

B. *T. verrucosum* var. album after three weeks.

C. *T. verrucosum* var. ochraceum after four weeks.

D. Slide culture preparation, stained with lactophenol cotton blue, showing macroconidia, clusters of microconidia, and chains of chlamydospores. X 400.

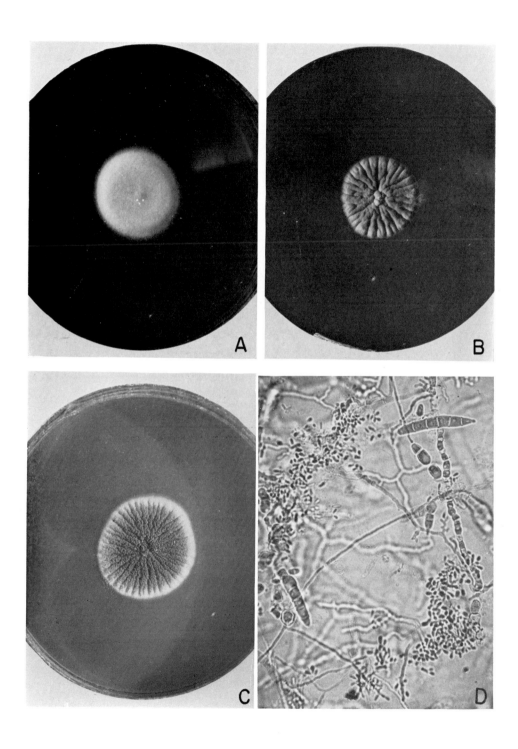

Trichophyton schoenleini

Media for Development of Significant Characters

MACROSCOPIC	
Sabouraud's glucose agar.	Glabrous, heaped and folded, sometimes showing a white powdery surface.

MICROSCOPIC	
Sabouraud's glucose agar.	Favic chandeliers, chlamydospores.

TRICHOPHYTON SCHOENLEINI

(Achorion schoenleini)

THE FUNGUS *Trichophyton schoenleini* is the chief agent of favus, a chronic fungus infection of the scalp and sometimes of the glabrous skin and nails. The disease is rare in the United States. In infected hairs large endothrix spores in chains are found, together with mycelial elements and characteristic air bubbles. The species can be isolated on Sabouraud's glucose medium, but may be difficult to obtain in pure form due to bacterial contamination of the inoculum.

Cultural and Microscopic Characteristics

The colony on Sabouraud's glucose agar is slow-growing, glabrous, heaped and folded, the surface later becoming covered with short, white, aerial mycelium; a characteristic of the colony is the cracking of the medium.

Microscopically, the identifying structures are the "favic chandeliers."

TRICHOPHYTON SCHOENLEINI

Figure 8

A. Colony on Sabouraud's glucose agar after four weeks.

B. Sabouraud's glucose agar slide culture preparation, showing "favic chandeliers." X 400.

TRICHOPHYTON VIOLACEUM

Media for Development of Significant Characters

MACROSCOPIC	
Sabouraud's glucose agar.	Glabrous, heaped and folded, deep violet in color, sometimes showing fine, white, velvety mycelium on surface.

MICROSCOPIC	
Sabouraud's glucose agar.	No identifying structures.

TRICHOPHYTON VIOLACEUM

THE SPECIES *Trichophyton violaceum* attacks the hair of the scalp and bearded areas, the skin, and nails. The infection is found chiefly in immigrants in the United States, and causes one of the most refractory types of ringworm of the scalp of all the trichophyta. The hairs show the endothrix type of infection, the large spores being arranged in rows within the hair shaft. The microorganism can be isolated on Sabouraud's glucose agar, but growth may not be recognizable for three to four weeks.

Cultural and Microscopic Characteristics

The colony on Sabouraud's glucose medium is moist, glabrous, heaped and folded, and shows a deep violet color, the surface at times becoming covered with a fine, white, short, aerial mycelium.

Microscopically, no identifying structures are found.

TRICHOPHYTON VIOLACEUM

Figure 9

A. Colony on Sabouraud's glucose agar after four weeks.

B. Hair from ringworm of scalp showing endothrix spores. X 600.

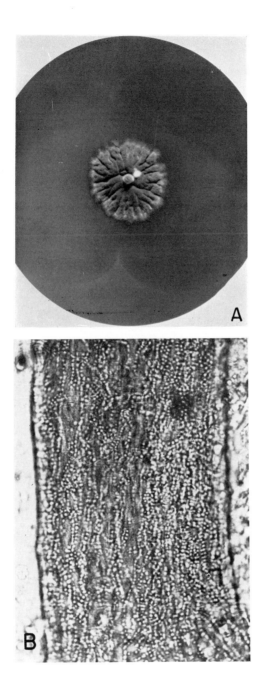

EPIDERMOPHYTON FLOCCOSUM

Media for Development of Significant Characters

MACROSCOPIC	
Sabouraud's glucose agar.	Velvety or felt-like surface with or without radial grooves; greenish-yellow in color.

MICROSCOPIC	
Sabouraud's glucose agar. Corn meal.	Macroconidia, chlamydospores.

EPIDERMOPHYTON

THE GENUS *Epidermophyton* consists of a single species, *E. floccosum* (*E. inguinale, E. cruris*). This dermatophyte attacks the skin, particularly of the groin, and the nails. The hair is not affected.

Cultural and Microscopic Characteristics

The colony on Sabouraud's glucose agar is moderately fast-growing; the surface is velvety or felt-like, often with radial furrows and an irregular, folded center, or the surface may be smooth; the color is greenish-yellow. A characteristic of this culture is the appearance on its surface of small tufts of white, fluffy, aerial mycelium.

Microscopically, there will be seen the distinctive clavate macroconidia with blunt ends; they are smooth, thin-walled, and multiseptate, and are frequently borne in banana-like clusters; numerous intercalary and terminal chlamydospores are also characteristic; no microconidia are produced.

Epidermophyton floccosum

Figure 10

A. Colony on Sabouraud's glucose agar after four weeks.

B. Cluster of multiseptate, club-shaped macroconidia on Sabouraud's glucose agar. X 400.

C. Numerous typical club-shaped macroconidia. X 400.

D. Chlamydospores. X 600.

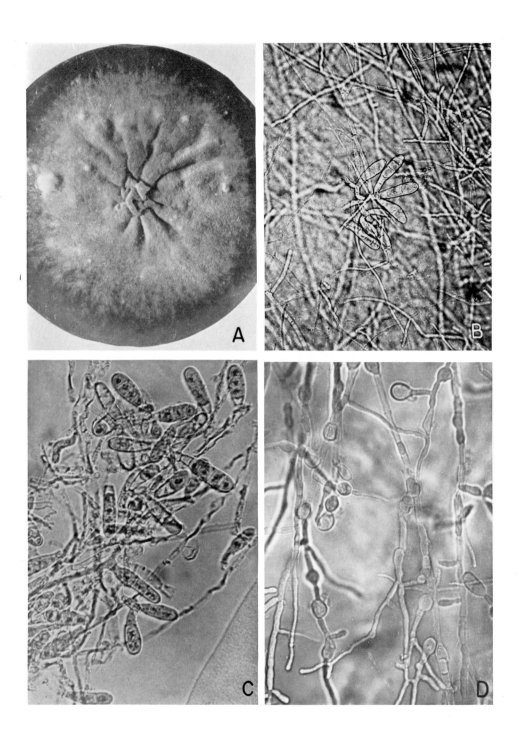

Deep-Seated Mycoses

(Subcutaneous; Systemic)

ALMOST ALL THE deep-seated mycoses have been encountered throughout the North American continent, although the incitants are not necessarily endemic in all the areas where the diseases have been found. Shifting populations and travel in endemic areas play a large part in the appearance of some of these diseases in areas where they are totally unsuspected. As a consequence, these infections frequently remain undiagnosed or are incorrectly diagnosed.

These diseases, which may be fatal or relatively benign, are localized or systemic, and are usually chronic, but may be acute or subacute. They are caused by a wide variety of fungi.

These fungi attack the internal organs of the body, bone, meninges, subcutaneous tissue, skin, and mucous membranes. A definitive diagnosis cannot be established without the aid of the laboratory, since demonstration of the fungus in pathologic specimens, either by microscopic examination or cultural isolation, is essential.

A number of the most important fungi are described in the following pages under the specific diseases which they incite.

ACTINOMYCES BOVIS

Media for Development of Significant Characters

MACROSCOPIC	
Beef-heart infusion agar with blood (anaerobic 7 to 10 days).	Colonies—white, raised, rough, dry, 1 mm. or less in diameter with irregular surface and lobate edges.
Beef-infusion agar with 1% glucose in test tube* (aerobic incubation).	No growth for 5 to 15 mm. below surface; at upper level of growth definite band from 2 to 7 mm. in width, consisting of minute colonies; below this many discrete colonies of variable size and of irregular shape.
Beef-infusion broth with 1% glucose (anaerobic 7 to 10 days).	Good growth, clear supernatant, floccular or granular sediment; tiny colonies up sides of tube.

MICROSCOPIC	
Beef-heart infusion agar with blood (anaerobic).	Gram-positive, branching filaments, long and short rods, coccoid forms.
Beef-infusion broth with 1% glucose (anaerobic 7 to 10 days).	Gram-positive, branching filaments, pleomorphic rods, coccoid bodies.

* Glucose-agar shake tube.

Actinomycosis

Actinomycosis is one of the most common of the deep mycoses. The infection may be localized or generalized, and it may spread by continuity or through the blood stream. It most commonly occurs in the head and neck, but may occur in any part of the body. Characteristically, granulomatous lesions are produced. The etiologic agent is *Actinomyces bovis*.

Specimens for Examination

Pus, sputum, cerebrospinal fluid, urine, biopsy or post-mortem materials may be submitted.

Cultural and Microscopic Characteristics

A. bovis is an anaerobic or microaerophilic, Gram-positive, non-acid-fast, filamentous microorganism which shows true branching and which readily breaks up into bacillary and coccoid forms. In pus from tissue and in tissue sections, it is found in the form of granules, lobulated structures composed of masses of branching filaments with a periphery, usually, of radiating "clubs."

The microorganism can be isolated on brain-heart infusion agar or beef-heart infusion agar with blood at 35 to 37° C. The colonies on the latter medium are exceedingly slow-growing, white, raised and rough, having an irregular surface and lobate edges; they are embedded in the medium, removable intact and difficult to emulsify. Microscopically, in film preparations stained by Gram's method, there will be seen pleomorphic Gram-positive rods and filaments showing true branching.

Pathogenicity for Animals

This microorganism has very slight, if any, pathogenicity for the common laboratory animal. It is pathogenic for the male hamster (3 to 4 weeks old), and when mixed with gastric mucin will infect male albino mice (10 to 15 days old).

ACTINOMYCES BOVIS

Figure 11

A. Colonies on blood agar after two weeks' incubation under anaerobic conditions.

B. Stained film preparation of culture from blood agar. X 780.

C. Stained film preparation of pus from abscess in experimentally infected hamster. X 600.

D. Unstained granules with clubs in pus from encapsulated abscess in experimentally infected hamster. X 600.

E. Section of encapsulated abscess, showing granules with clubs and mass of filaments. H. & E. X 900.

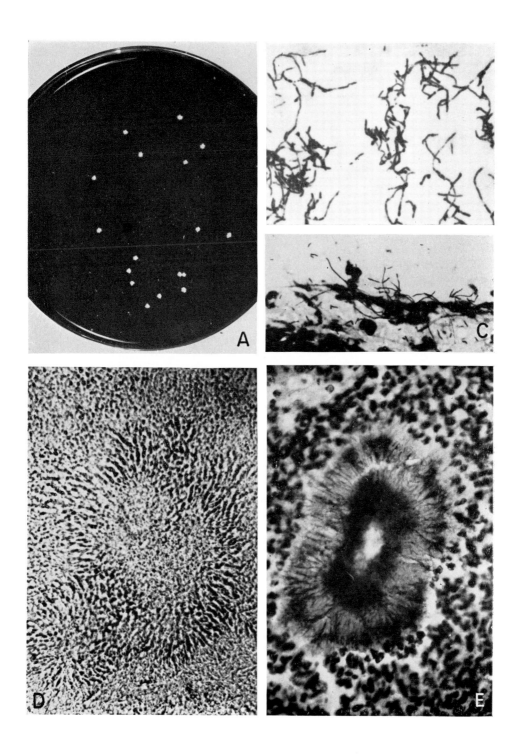

Nocardia asteroides

Media for Development of Significant Characters

MACROSCOPIC

Sabouraud's glucose agar slants (22-25° or 37° C.).	Raised, wrinkled, granular growth, ochre to yellow to orange in color, sometimes becoming covered with chalky-white aerial mycelium.
Gelatin.	No liquefaction after 2 to 4 weeks at 22-25° or 37° C.
Milk containing bromcresol purple or litmus as indicator.	Surface pellicle, no coagulation, no peptonization, alkaline reaction after 4 weeks at 22-25° or 37° C.

MICROSCOPIC

Sabouraud's glucose agar.	Gram-positive branching filaments, fragmenting filaments, bacillary and coccoid forms.
Milk with indicator (3 weeks at 22-25° C.).	Acid-fast fragmenting filaments, bacillary and coccoid forms.

Nocardiosis

Nocardiosis is a disease similar to, or even clinically indistinguishable from, actinomycosis. The etiologic agent may be one of several species of the genus *Nocardia. N. asteroides* is the most commonly encountered species in the United States and is therefore described below.

Specimens for Examination

Pus, sputum, cerebrospinal fluid, biopsy specimens or post-mortem material may be submitted.

Cultural and Microscopic Characteristics

N. asteroides is an aerobic, Gram-positive, acid-fast, filamentous, branching microorganism which breaks up readily into short rods or coccoid forms. In sputum, pus or other exudates, it occurs in these forms. In abscesses it may also be found in the form of granules with or without peripheral clubs. The acid-fast property of this species is relatively feeble as compared with the tubercle bacillus. In culture this property can best be demonstrated by growing the microorganism in skim milk.

The microorganism is easily isolated on Sabouraud's glucose agar at 22-25° or 37° C. The colony on this medium is slow-growing, dry, wrinkled, and granular with a slightly heaped center and an irregular, lobulate margin; the color is at first whitish, changing to ochre and later to orange, sometimes becoming covered with a chalky-white aerial mycelium. In film preparations stained by Gram's method there will be seen long and short, Gram-positive, branching filaments, fragmenting filaments, short bacillary and coccoid forms.

Pathogenicity for Animals

The microorganism has a high degree of pathogenicity for the guinea pig.

NOCARDIA ASTEROIDES

Figure 12

A. Colony on Sabouraud's glucose agar after four weeks.

B. Stained film preparation of culture in milk, showing acid-fast filaments and rods. X 1500.

C. Stained film preparation of pus from omentum of experimentally infected guinea pig, showing fragmenting, branching filaments. X 600.

D. Section of guinea pig omentum, showing abscess with central granule. H. & E. X 600.

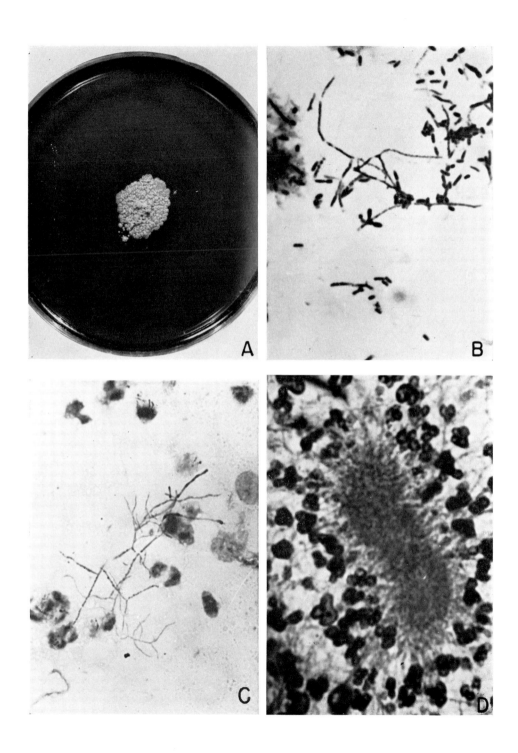

BLASTOMYCES DERMATITIDIS

Media for Development of Significant Characters

MACROSCOPIC	
Blood agar (37° C.).	Cream to tan, soft, wrinkled and waxy in appearance.
Sabouraud's glucose agar (22-25° C.).	White, fluffy, aerial mycelium, becoming cream to tan.

MICROSCOPIC	
Blood agar (37° C.).	Large, round, single budding, thick-walled cells.
Sabouraud's glucose agar (22-25° C.).	Round to pyriform microconidia borne laterally on hyphae.

BLASTOMYCOSIS

North American Blastomycosis (Gilchrist Disease)

THIS IS A CHRONIC DISEASE which may be localized or systemic. It is often localized in the skin, forming granulomatous lesions with a verrucous surface and a raised smooth border sloping sharply to the normal skin. The systemic form usually follows a primary pulmonary infection and may spread by the blood stream, affecting any other organ or tissue of the body. The etiologic agent is *Blastomyces dermatitidis*.

Specimens for Examination

Bits of tissue from skin lesions, pus from subcutaneous abscesses, sputum, bone, blood, or cerebrospinal fluid may be submitted.

Cultural and Microscopic Characteristics

B. dermatitidis exhibits dimorphism, i.e., it grows in one form in tissue and in another form on culture media. In pathologic material it appears as a large, spherical, thick-walled, budding cell of variable size, 8 to 20μ in diameter; on Sabouraud's glucose agar at room temperature it appears in the mycelial form.

On blood agar medium at 37° C. the growth is soft, wrinkled, and waxy in appearance, cream to tan in color, while on Sabouraud's glucose medium at room temperature the growth consists of white, downy or fluffy, aerial mycelium, later becoming cream to tan to brown.

Microscopically, the culture on blood agar medium at 37° C. appears in the same form as in tissue, while on Sabouraud's glucose medium the growth consists of branched, septate hyphae on which are borne small, round to pear-shaped conidia, sessile or on short lateral branches.

A culture thought to be *B. dermatitidis* should not be identified as such without demonstration of its dimorphic nature.

Pathogenicity for Animals

The microorganism is pathogenic for the young male hamster and to a lesser degree for the white mouse, guinea pig, and rabbit.

BLASTOMYCES DERMATITIDIS

Figure 13

A. Colony on Sabouraud's glucose agar after three weeks at room temperature.

B. Culture after 72 hours on blood agar at 37° C.

C. Culture mount of growth on blood agar. X 800.

D. Sabouraud's glucose agar slide culture preparation, showing small, round to pear-shaped conidia. X 400.

E. Large, spherical, thick-walled, budding cells of variable size in lung tissue of man, stained by Hotchkiss-McManus technique. X 400.

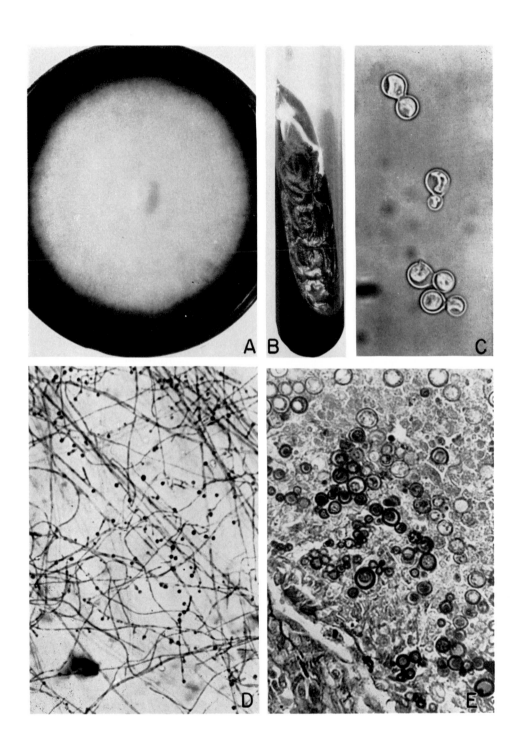

Blastomycosis

South American Blastomycosis (Lutz-Splendore-Almeida's Disease)

THIS IS A chronic granulomatous disease of many manifestations, depending upon the tissue involved. It may remain localized or become disseminated. Initial lesions, while commonest on the mucous membrane of the mouth and pharynx, may also be localized on the nasal or anorectal membrane, the skin, and in the lungs; frequently the larynx is infected from the lungs. Dissemination takes place by the hematogenous and lymphatic routes. The etiologic agent is *Paracoccidioides brasiliensis (Blastomyces brasiliensis)*.

Specimens for Examination

Bits of tissue from cutaneous or mucosal lesions, pus from lymph nodes or from cutaneous abscesses, sputum, bone, blood, biopsy material, or tissues from post-mortem examinations may be submitted.

Cultural and Microscopic Characteristics

P. brasiliensis is a dimorphic fungus. In pathologic materials, the microorganism appears in the form of single and multiple budding, thick-walled, yeastlike cells, 10 to 60μ in diameter, and on artificial medium at room temperature, in a mold-like or mycelial form.

On blood agar or chocolate agar at 37° C. the colonies are white, yeastlike, and cerebriform; on Sabouraud's glucose agar at room temperature, the colony is compact, irregularly folded and covered with a short-napped, white, aerial mycelium, becoming brownish in old cultures.

Microscopically, the growth on blood agar at 37° C. consists of many single and multiple budding cells identical with the tissue forms, while on Sabouraud's glucose medium the growth at room temperature is composed of branched, septate hyphae on which are borne a few pyriform conidia, sessile, or on short stalks.

A mycelial culture thought to be *P. brasiliensis* should not be identified as such without conversion to the yeast phase and demonstration of multiple budding cells.

Pathogenicity for Animals

The microorganism has been reported as pathogenic for the guinea pig, rabbit, hamster, and white mouse.

Paracoccidioides brasiliensis

Figure 14

A. Colony on Sabouraud's glucose agar after three weeks at room temperature.

B. Growth on blood agar after seventy-two hours at 37° C.

C. Culture mount from blood agar at 37° C., in lactophenol cotton blue. X 600.

D. Large spherical, thick-walled single and multiple budding cells in human tissue. H. & E. X 800. (Courtesy of Dr. Margarita Silva, Department of Dermatology, College of Physicians and Surgeons, Columbia University, New York, N.Y.).

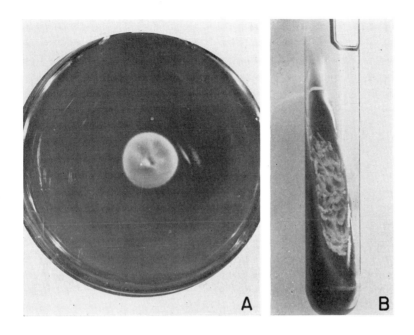

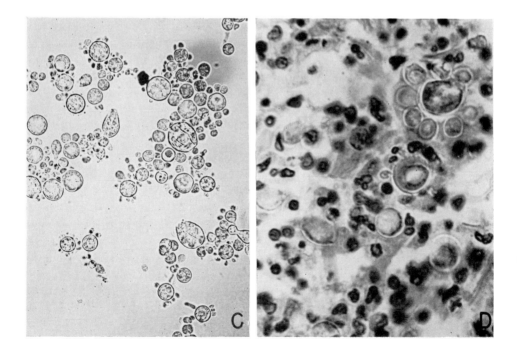

Candida albicans

Media for Development of Significant Characters

MACROSCOPIC	
Sabouraud's glucose agar.	Creamy, pasty, smooth.

MICROSCOPIC	
Sabouraud's glucose agar.	Round to oval budding cells.
Corn meal agar dispensed in Petri plates.	Mycelium, blastospores, chlamydospores.

Moniliasis (candidiasis)

Moniliasis is a disease of many manifestations. It may involve the skin, particularly the intertriginous areas, nails (onychia), and tissue around the nails (paronychia), the mucous membranes (mouth, pharynx, vagina), the perianal area, bronchopulmonary system, or even the blood stream or meninges. The chief etiologic agent is *Candida albicans;* other species which may cause infection are *C. tropicalis, C. guilliermondi, C. parapsilosis, C. pseudotropicalis,* and *C. krusei. C. albicans,* because of its greater importance, is described in more detail. A table with the differential characteristics of the six species is included.

Specimens for Examination

Skin and nail scrapings, exudates from mucous membranes, sputum, feces, blood or cerebrospinal fluid may be required for examination.

Cultural and Microscopic Characteristics

C. albicans is a budding yeastlike microorganism which forms a true mycelium as well as pseudomycelium. It appears in pathologic materials as budding cells and mycelial elements.

It is easily isolated on Sabouraud's glucose agar. The colony is cream-colored, pasty, and smooth, and has a yeastlike odor. Microscopically, there are found budding cells of varying shape which are of little aid in the specific identification of the microorganism.

For identification the demonstration of the large, round, thick-walled chlamydospore characteristic of *C. albicans* is essential. This may be accomplished by growing the microorganism on corn meal agar. The corn meal agar dispensed in Petri plates should be inoculated with the primary culture by cutting through the agar along the line of streak and incubating at room temperature for several days. Along the line of streaks *C. albicans* develops mycelium on which is produced grape-like clusters of blastospores and the round-thick-walled chlamydospores characteristic of this species.

Pathogenicity for Animals

This fungus is pathogenic for mice and rabbits.

CANDIDA ALBICANS

Figure 15

A. Colony on Sabouraud's glucose agar after two weeks.

B. Culture mount from Sabouraud's agar. X 800.

C. Culture mount from corn meal agar, showing clusters of blasto-spores and large, round, thick-walled cells (chlamydospores) along hyphae. X 400.

D. Budding cells and mycelial elements in skin scrapings, stained by Hotchkiss-McManus technique. X 400. (Preparation courtesy of Mr. J. Dennis Pollack of the Department of Dermatology, College of Physicians and Surgeons, Columbia University.)

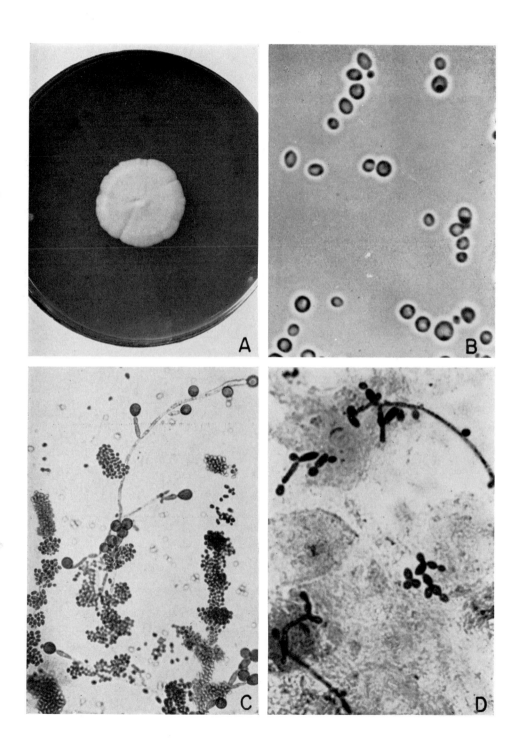

DIFFERENTIAL CHARACTERISTICS OF CANDIDA SPECIES [*]
Figure 16

Microorganism	Sabouraud's glucose agar culture	Sabouraud's glucose broth culture	Microscopic morphology corn meal	Sugar reactions D	M	S	L
1. *Candida albicans*	Cream-colored, pasty, smooth colony or with mycelial border.	Growth bottom of tube.	Spherical or ball-like clusters of blastospores along mycelium, chlamydospores simple or in grape-like clusters at room temperature. At 37° C. no chlamydospores.	AG	AG	A or	O or O
2. *Candida tropicalis*	Cream-colored, membranous, folded colony.	Heavy growth at bottom of tube; mucous-like ring on surface.	Blastospores single or in chains or irregular clusters anywhere along hyphal thread. No or very few chlamydospores.	AG	AG	AG	O
3. *Candida guilliermondi*	Like *C. albicans*	No surface growth.	Fine mycelium, elongated cells, clusters small.	AG	O	AG	O
4. *Candida parapsilosis* (*C. parakrusei*)	Cream-colored, pasty, smooth colony.	Growth bottom of tube, no ring.	Fine and coarse branched mycelium i.e. giant forms. Blastospores single or in short chains or whorls from distal ends of cells.	AG	O	O	O
5. *Candida pseudo-tropicalis* (*C. mortifera*)	Thin, grey, pasty colony.	No surface growth.	Elongated cells joined end to end, readily separated; blastospores not much differentiated from hyphal cells.	AG	O	AG	AG
6. *Candida krusei*	Dull, flat, white colony.	Definite film at surface.	Elongated cells forming branched mycelium, easily disintegrated. Blastospores elongated, in whorls at distal ends of hyphal cells.	AG	O	O	O

[*] By permission of the late Dr. Rhoda Benham (of Columbia University) from her laboratory manual (Revised).

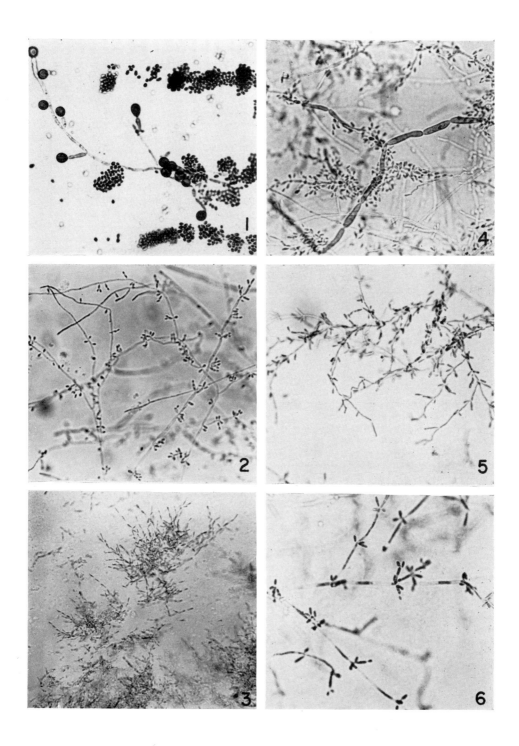

Coccidioides immitis

Media for Development of Significant Characters

MACROSCOPIC	
Sabouraud's glucose agar.	White, cottony, aerial mycelium, becoming tan with age, having a central zone of flat, sparse mycelium.

MICROSCOPIC	
Sabouraud's glucose agar.	Coarse, branching hyphae and chains of thick-walled chlamydospores.

COCCIDIOIDOMYCOSIS

COCCIDIOIDOMYCOSIS, caused by *Coccidioides immitis,* occurs in two forms — an acute self-limiting respiratory infection (California disease, valley fever), and a chronic, sometimes fatal, disease (coccidioidal granuloma) involving the cutaneous, subcutaneous, visceral and bony tissues.

Specimens for Examination

Exudates from cutaneous lesions, pus from abscesses, sputum, cerebrospinal fluid, blood, biopsy material, or tissues from postmortem examination may be submitted.

Cultural and Microscopic Characteristics

C. immitis is dimorphic. In the parasitic phase it appears as thick-walled, endosporulating spherules, 5 to 50μ in diameter, in different stages of development. In culture at 37° C. or at room temperature it occurs only in the mycelial form.

The microorganism is easily isolated on Sabouraud's glucose medium or on Mycosel agar if the specimen is grossly contaminated. The colony is moderately fast-growing, flat, moist, and membranous, later developing a coarse, white to tan to brown, cottony, aerial mycelium with central zone of flat, sparse mycelium.

Microscopically, the culture shows coarse, branching hyphae, some broken up into thick-walled spores, chlamydospores, usually in chains.

Great precaution should be exercised when handling these cultures, since the chlamydospores are easily dislodged and carried through the air. Cultures on medium in Petri plates should not be employed; Petroff flasks (22 x 95 mm.) or tubes should be used instead.

Pathogenicity for Animals

This fungus is pathogenic for white mice, guinea pigs, and rabbits. The guinea pig injected intratesticularly with a suspension of the chlamydospores develops a severe orchitis within seven to ten days. From such lesions pus may be aspirated and the typical endosporulating spherules demonstrated by direct microscopic examination.

A culture thought to be *C. immitis* should not be identified as such without demonstration of transformation in a susceptible animal of the chlamydospores to the characteristic parasitic growth phase (thick-walled endosporulating spherules).

Coccidioides immitis

Figure 17

A. Colony on Sabouraud's glucose agar after five weeks.

B. Culture mount showing chains of chlamydospores. X 400.

C. Same. X 800.

D. Section from testicle of experimentally infected guinea pig, showing endosporulating spherules. H. & E. X 400.

E. Spherule. X 800.

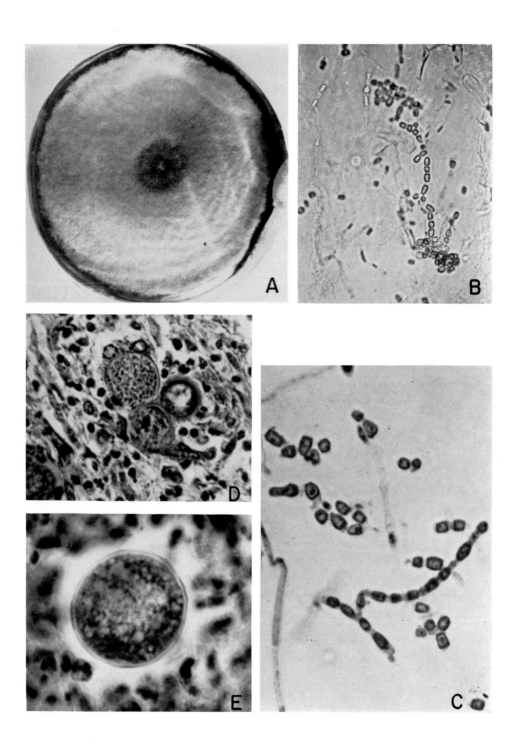

CRYPTOCOCCUS NEOFORMANS

Media for Development of Significant Characters

MACROSCOPIC	
Sabouraud's glucose agar (22-25° and 37° C.).	Cream to tan in color, usually mucoid and glossy, occasionally dry and dull.

MICROSCOPIC	
Sabouraud's glucose agar.	Round, budding cells of varying size surrounded by capsules of different diameters.

CRYPTOCOCCOSIS

CRYPTOCOCCOSIS is a subacute or chronic infection chiefly of the central nervous system, but may involve almost any part of the body. The etiologic agent is *Cryptococcus neoformans (Torula histolytica)*.

Specimens for Examination

Cerebrospinal fluid, scrapings from superficial skin lesions, pus from subcutaneous abscesses, sputum, bone, lymph nodes, blood, bone marrow, or specimens collected at post-mortem may be submitted.

Cultural and Microscopic Characteristics

Cryptococcus neoformans is a budding yeastlike microorganism. In pathologic material and in culture it appears as a round, occasionally oval, budding cell of variable size, 4 to 15μ in diameter, surrounded by a refractile mucinous capsule. The capsule varies in width, sometimes being twice the diameter of the cell, and can be demonstrated by mounting a loopful of the infected material or culture in a drop of India ink.

The fungus is easily isolated on Sabouraud's glucose medium. The colony is mucoid and slimy and is cream to brownish in color.

The pathogenic strains grow readily at 22-25° and 37° C. and do not assimilate KNO_3, while the nonpathogenic or avirulent strains grow poorly, if at all, at 37° C. and assimilate KNO_3.

Pathogenicity for Animals

The microorganism is virulent for white mice and rats. For proof of the virulence of a given strain of *C. neoformans*, mice should be injected intravenously or intracerebrally, and, following the death of the animal, budding cells with large capsules demonstrated in the brain.

CRYPTOCOCCUS NEOFORMANS

Figure 18

A. Colony on Sabouraud's glucose agar after 10 days.

B. Culture mount from Sabouraud's agar in drop of lactophenol.
                                                              X 450.

C. India ink preparation of culture from Sabouraud's agar. X 400.

D. Section of spleen from white rat, showing budding cells, sur-rounded by capsules. H. & E. X 525.

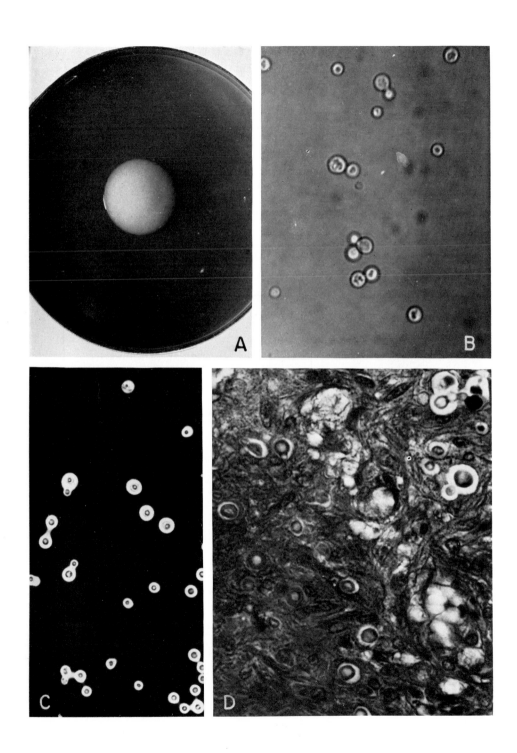

GEOTRICHUM CANDIDUM

Media for Development of Significant Characters

MACROSCOPIC	
Sabouraud's glucose agar.	Flat, membranous, soft, yeastlike consistency, white to cream in color.
Honey broth.	White pellicle.

MICROSCOPIC	
Sabouraud's glucose agar. Corn meal agar.	Chains of rectangular to round arthrospores.

GEOTRICHOSIS

GEOTRICHOSIS is a comparatively rare and mild disease. Lesions may occur in the mucous membranes of the mouth and intestinal tract, in the bronchi and lungs. The etiologic agent is *Geotrichum candidum*.

This microorganism may be present on the skin, in the mouth, and in the feces of normal persons, or as a secondary invader in pulmonary disease, particularly tuberculosis. A diagnosis of bronchial or pulmonary geotrichosis should therefore not be made without repeated demonstration of the presence of the fungus in the sputum by both microscopic and cultural examination, and the elimination of other bronchopulmonary diseases.

Specimens for Examination

Exudates from lesions in the mouth, sputum, or bloody stools may be submitted.

Cultural and Microscopic Characteristics

G. candidum appears in pathologic material as large, rectangular to oval cells (arthrospores) and round, thick-walled, nonbudding cells. It can be easily isolated on Sabouraud's glucose agar.

The colony on the Sabouraud's medium is flat, membranous, soft, of yeastlike consistency, white to cream in color, and closely adherent to the medium. A differential feature is the formation of a white pellicle in liquid medium.

Microscopically, it reveals broad, septate mycelium and chains of rectangular to round arthrospores formed by fragmentation of the hyphae.

Pathogenicity for Animals

Pathogenicity for laboratory animals has not been demonstrated.

Geotrichum candidum

Figure 19

A. Colony on Sabouraud's glucose agar after three weeks.

B. Slide culture preparation on corn meal agar stained with lacto-phenol cotton blue, showing arthrospore formation. X 400.

C and D. Same, showing rectangular and round arthrospores. X 800.

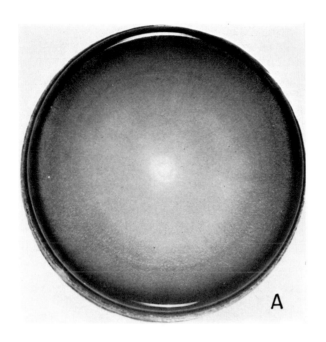

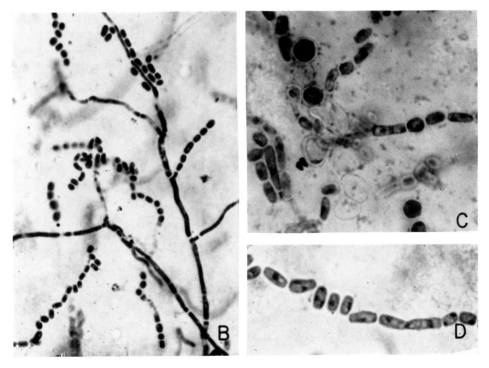

Histoplasma capsulatum

Media for Development of Significant Characters

MACROSCOPIC

Blood agar (37° C.).	Moist, white yeastlike growth.
Sabouraud's glucose agar(22-25° C.).	White, fluffy, aerial mycelium, gradually becoming tan to brown.

MICROSCOPIC

Blood agar (37° C.).	Small, oval, budding cells.
Potato-glucose agar (22-25° C.).	Round to pyriform microconidia borne laterally on hyphae and large, thick-walled tuberculate chlamydospores (macroconidia).

Histoplasmosis

Histoplasmosis is a localized or generalized infection, essentially of the reticuloendothelial system, and may be acute, subacute, or chronic, involving almost any organ of the body. The incitant is found chiefly as an intracellular parasite of the mononuclear cells in the peripheral blood, sternal bone marrow, lymph nodes, or spleen. The etiologic agent is *Histoplasma capsulatum*.

Specimens for Examination

Tissue obtained by biopsy of lesions from skin, mucous membranes and lymph nodes, sputum, gastric washings, or tissue from post-mortem examination, including the brain, may be submitted.

Cultural and Microscopic Characteristics

H. capsulatum is dimorphic. In parasitized tissue it is found as small, oval, yeastlike cells, 2-5μ in the longer diameter, within the large monocytes; on Sabouraud's glucose agar at room temperature it appears in the mycelial form.

Colonies on blood agar at 37° C. are small, white, yeastlike; on Sabouraud's glucose agar at room temperature they are downy or cottony and white to cream, later becoming tan to brown.

Microscopically, the culture on blood agar at 37° C. occurs in the same form as in tissue, while on Sabouraud's glucose agar it consists of septate hyphae on which are borne two types of spores: (1) small, smooth-walled, round to pyriform conidia, sessile on the sides of the hyphae or on very short lateral branches; (2) characteristic large, thick-walled, spiny or tuberculate chlamydospores (macroconidia).

For the identification of a culture thought to be *H. capsulatum*, the demonstration of the dimorphic nature of the fungus, as well as the presence of the tuberculate chlamydospores, is essential.

Pathogenicity for Animals

This fungus is pathogenic for mice, young hamsters, guinea pigs, and rabbits.

Histoplasma capsulatum

Figure 20

A. Colony on Sabouraud's glucose agar after three weeks at room temperature.

B. Growth on blood agar after 72 hours at 37° C.

C. Growth from blood agar at 37° C., in lactophenol. X 400.

D. Culture from potato-glucose agar, showing small, smooth-walled, round to pyriform conidia and tuberculate chlamydospores. X 400.

E. Large, thick-walled, tuberculate chlamydospores, stained with lactophenol cotton blue. X 1000.

F. Granulomatous lesion from ear of experimentally infected rabbit, showing multinucleated giant cell filled with *H. capsulatum*. H. & E. X 1500.

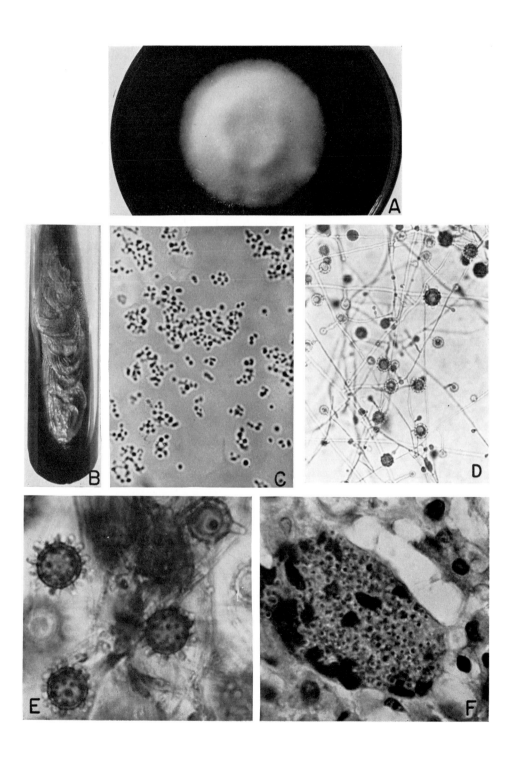

Aspergillosis

Aspergillosis is an inflammatory granulomatous infection. The skin, nails, external auditory canal, paranasal sinuses, eye, bronchi, bone, meninges, and brain may be involved. Several species of *Aspergillus* have been incriminated as agents of the disease: *A. fumigatus, A. flavus, A. nidulans, A. glaucus,* and *A. niger. A. fumigatus* is by far the most frequently encountered. These fungi are ubiquitous in nature and are commonly saprophytic; for reasons not understood, they may become pathogenic and incite infection.

Pulmonary aspergillosis as a primary infection is well recognized and occurs most often in agricultural workers, squab feeders, fur cleaners, and other persons in contact with fungus-contaminated grain. Its occurrence as a complication of bacterial infection of the lungs has become increasingly important with the widespread use of antibiotics, steroids, and folic acid antagonists. The portal of entry is usually the respiratory tract from which the infection may become widely disseminated and terminate fatally.

Specimens for Examination

Sputum, skin, material from ear, and biopsy and post-mortem specimens may be submitted.

The disease is difficult to diagnose with certainty since the causative agent, usually *A. fumigatus,* is extremely widespread in nature and may appear in culture media or in pathologic specimens as a contaminant. The mere isolation or even the identification of the fungus is not sufficient. Demonstration of the fungus in tissue by direct microscopic examination is essential.

Cultural and Microscopic Characteristics

A. fumigatus is a filamentous fungus. In sputum or tissue, it appears as short, branching hyphal fragments, often with many small (2 to 4μ), round, green spores scattered throughout the field; occasionally the entire fruiting structure may be present. The fungus is easily isolated on Sabouraud's glucose agar at room temperature or at 37° C. Where there is marked bacterial contamination, streptomycin and penicillin should be added to this medium. Medium to which cycloheximide (Actidione) has been added should not be used. The colony is fast-growing, white at first, soon becoming green or dark green, flat, and velvety. The fungus grows well at 45° C. or higher.

Microscopically, the identifying structure of this species, as well as all species of *Aspergillus*, is the conidiophore with the large terminal vesicle bearing many sterigmata (phialides) from which chains of spores are produced. The conidiophore of *A. fumigatus* is smooth-walled, and the conidial head, columnar and compact, with sterigmata in one series; conidia are globose, green and echinulate.

Pathogenicity for Animals

The fungus is pathogenic to a high degree for the rabbit and to a lesser extent for the guinea pig.

ASPERGILLUS FUMIGATUS

Figure 21

A. Colony on Sabouraud's glucose agar, seven days at room temperature.

B. Slide culture preparation on corn meal agar, showing conidial heads. X 600.

C. Section from human lung showing septate hyphae. H. & E. X 400.

D. Same section showing conidial head (arrow). X 800 (Courtesy of Dr. J. Lebowich, Saratoga County Laboratory, Saratoga Springs, N.Y.).

E. Hyphal fragment of A. *fumigatus* in sputum. (Reprinted with permission from Skinner, C. E., Emmons, C. W., Tsuchiya, H. M.: Henrici's Yeasts, Molds, and Actinomycetes, 1947, John Wiley & Sons, Inc.)

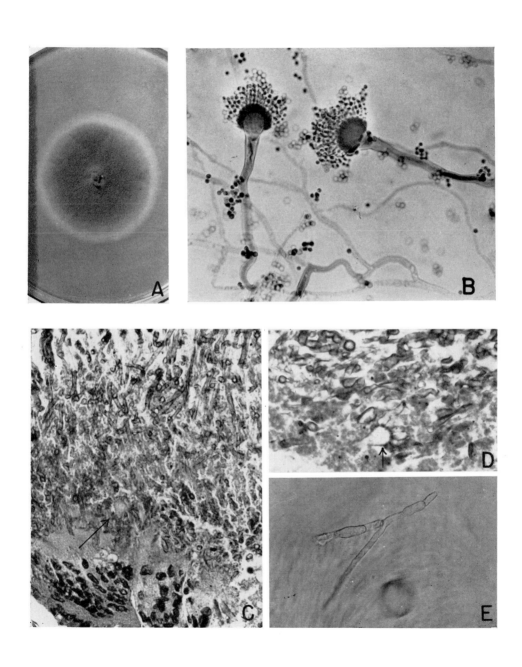

Systemic mucormycosis

Systemic mucormycosis is a disease characterized by vascular invasion with growth of hyphae, thrombosis, infarction, and reactive inflammation of hemorrhagic exudative and minimal granulomatous character. The infection may be incited by any one of several species of three genera *(Mucor, Rhizopus,* and *Absidia)* of the order *Mucorales* of the class *Phycomycetes.* The disease is being seen with increasing frequency, the pulmonary and cerebral tissues being most commonly attacked, often with a fatal outcome. These fungi may attack other tissues such as orbital, nasal, and paranasal sinuses and intestine, and produce relatively mild unrecognized infection. From such sites dissemination may occur, with a rapidly fatal result.

These *Phycomycetes* are ubiquitous and usually saprophytic but under certain conditions apparently have the capacity to incite disease. Their spores become airborne and enter the nose, sinuses, and lungs by inhalation or the gastrointestinal tract on contaminated food.

There are several predisposing factors, acidotic diabetes mellitus, leukemia, and other debilitating diseases; the use of steroids, folic acid antagonists, and prolonged antibiotic therapy is also believed to enhance susceptibility.

Specimens for Examination

Materials from sinuses, sputum, pus, cerebrospinal fluid, and biopsy and post-mortem tissues may be submitted.

The laboratory diagnosis of mucormycosis is not easy and should be made only under carefully controlled conditions, since the etiologic agents are extremely widespread in nature and may appear as contaminants on media or in pathologic specimens. Demonstration of broad, nonseptate hyphae by direct microscopic examination of pathologic specimens, and isolation and identification of the fungus are essential for a definitive diagnosis.

Cultural and Microscopic Examination

The *Mucorales* are nonseptate, filamentous fungi. In sputum, pus, or tissue, they appear as wide (limits of 4 to 50μ), nonseptate, branching hyphal fragments; occasionally the entire fruiting structure may be found. They are easily isolated at room temperature on Sabouraud's glucose agar with the addition of streptomycin and penicillin or at 37° C. on blood medium with antibiotics. The colony grows rapidly, quickly filling a Petri plate or test tube with fluffy mycelium, first white, later dark gray.

Microscopically, the hyphae are wide, colorless, and coenocytic. The identifying structures are the single or branched sporangiophores which arise from any point on the hyphae or opposite rhizoids and bear large, terminal, globose, spore-filled structures, the sporangia. (See pages 132-133.)

Pathogenicity for Animals

The *Mucorales* have only slight, if any, pathogenicity for the normal rabbit. Cerebral mucormycosis has been produced experimentally in rabbits with alloxan-induced diabetes by intranasal instillation of spore suspensions of these fungi.

Agent of Mucormycosis

Figure 22

Section of human lung showing:

A. Wide, nonseptate hyphae in pulmonary artery. H. & E. X 300.

B. Same in lumen. X 700.

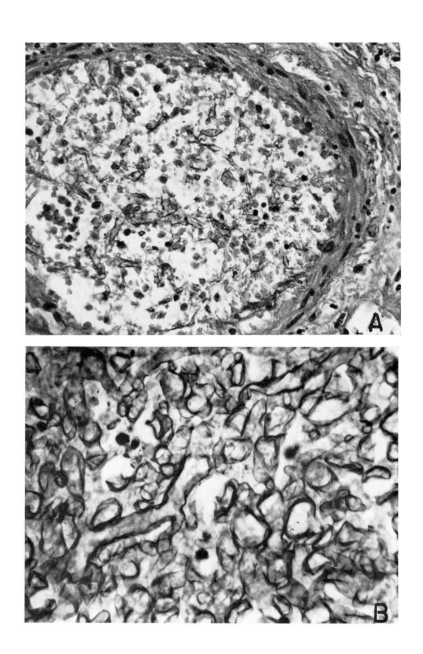

Monosporium apiospermum

Media for Development of Significant Characters

MACROSCOPIC	
Sabouraud's glucose agar.	White, cottony, aerial mycelium, becoming gray and spreading rapidly over entire surface of media, blackened undersurface.

MICROSCOPIC	
Corn meal agar.	Light brown, single, ovoid conidia, at tips of long or short conidiophores, occasionally on the sides of hyphae.

Maduromycosis

Maduromycosis is a chronic granulomatous disease, usually involving only one of the lower extremities, characterized by enlargement and deformity, multiple draining sinuses, and bone destruction. The material from discharging sinuses generally contains granules (grains), irregular-shaped masses of various colors, white, yellow, red or black. Among the incitants are species of *Madurella, Aspergillus, Cephalosporium, Allescheria,* and *Monosporium. M. apiospermum,* one of the chief incitants, is described below.

Specimens for Examination

Discharges from fistulae, material aspirated from deep cutaneous and subcutaneous nodules, may be submitted.

Cultural and Microscopic Characteristics

M. apiospermum is a filamentous fungus. In pathologic material the fungus appears in the form of yellowish-white granules, lobulated structures composed of wide septate hyphae with numerous peripheral chlamydospores.

It is readily isolated on Sabouraud's glucose agar at room temperature. The colony on this medium is fast-growing, white, cottony, gradually becoming gray, and has a grayish to black pigment on the undersurface.

Microscopically, there will be seen wide septate hyphae, and large, round, oval or clavate conidia, borne singly at tips of short or long conidiophores.

M. apiospermum is the imperfect form of *A. boydii,* also an etiologic agent of maduromycosis. *A. bodyii* produces asexual spores identical with *M. apiospermum;* for its identification, the demonstration of perithecia (ascocarps), large ($20\text{-}150\mu$), spherical, brown to black structures is essential. (See Figure 22C.)

Pathogenicity for Animals

The pathogenicity of these species for small laboratory animals has not been established.

Monosporium apiospermum

Figure 23

A. Colony on Sabouraud's glucose agar after five weeks.

B. Culture mount from corn meal agar stained with lactophenol cotton blue, showing single terminal conidia on long and short conidiophores. X 400.

C. Culture mount of *Allescheria boydii,* from Sabouraud's glucose agar, eight weeks, showing young and mature ascocarps; note large, ripe ascocarp discharging ascospores. X 800.

D. Granule from experimentally infected hamster. H. & E. X 800.

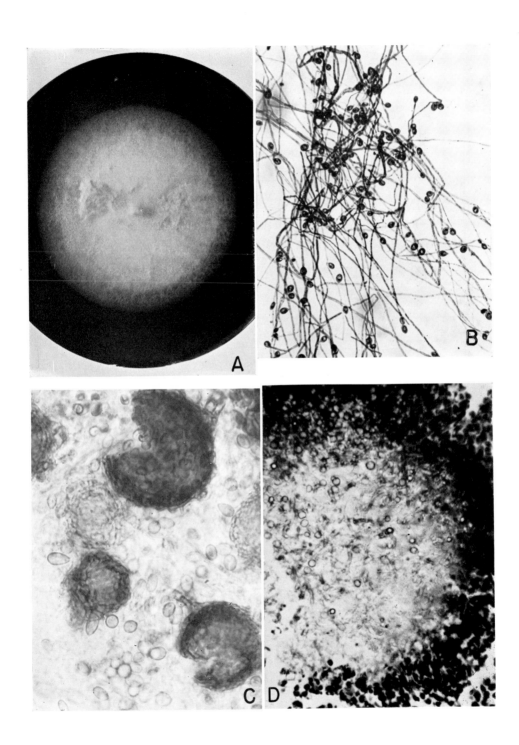

SPOROTRICHUM SCHENCKII

Media for Development of Significant Characters

MACROSCOPIC	
Glucose-cystine blood agar (37° C.).	Soft, yeastlike growth.
Sabouraud's glucose agar (22-25°C.).	Leathery, wrinkled and folded, tan to brown to black.

MICROSCOPIC	
Glucose-cystine blood agar (37° C.).	Round, oval, fusiform, budding cells.
Corn meal agar (22-25° C.).	Fine, septate hyphae and pear-shaped microconidia borne terminally in rosette-like clusters on lateral branches or singly along the hyphae.

Sporotrichosis

This disease is primarily a chronic infection of the skin and subcutaneous tissues, characterized by nodular lesions which spread along the regional lymphatics; generalized infections do occur, but are rare in the United States. The localized lesions are most frequently found on the extremities, particularly the hands. The etiologic agent is *Sporotrichum schenckii (S. beurmanni)*.

Specimens for Examination

Pus from subcutaneous nodules or from ulcerating lesions may be submitted.

Cultural and Microscopic Characteristics

S. schenckii is dimorphic. In pus and necrotic tissue from human infection, this microorganism appears as single-celled, cigar-shaped bodies, usually within the polymorphonuclear leucocytes (these structures are extremely difficult to demonstrate in pus or tissue sections from human lesions); on Sabouraud's glucose agar at room temperature it grows in the mycelial form.

On glucose-cystine blood agar at 37° C., the growth is creamy, white, soft, and yeastlike. On Sabouraud's glucose medium at room temperature the microorganism forms a mycelial colony, at first white and soft, later becoming tan to brown to black and leathery in texture, and having a convoluted center from which extend radial grooves terminating in a flat border. The appearance of the colony on this medium is diagnostic.

Microscopically, the culture on the blood medium at 37° C. is found in the same form as in tissue, while on Sabouraud's glucose medium the culture shows a fine, branching, septate mycelium and many small, pear-shaped conidia. The conidia are borne terminally in rosette-like clusters on lateral branches or are attached singly along the hyphae.

Pathogenicity for Animals

The fungus is infectious for white male rats and mice, and male hamsters (3 to 4 weeks old).

Sporotrichum schenckii

Figure 24

A. Dark brown to black colony on Sabouraud's glucose agar after three weeks at room temperature.

B. Culture mount of growth from glucose-cystine blood agar at 37° C. X 400.

C. Culture mount from corn meal, showing fine branching hyphae and pear-shaped conidia borne in rosette-like clusters at tips of lateral branches (conidiophores) and singly along sides of hyphae. X 600.

D. Section from testicle of experimentally infected hamster, showing Gram-positive, cigar-shaped bodies. Gram-Weigert. X 800.

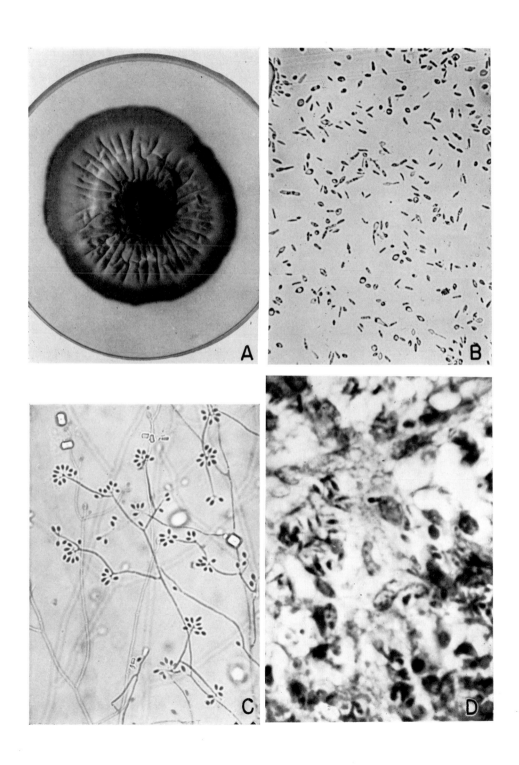

AGENTS OF CHROMOBLASTOMYCOSIS

MACROSCOPIC

(On Sabouraud's glucose agar)

Phialophora ver-rucosa
Cladosporium carionii
Fonsecaea pedrosoi
	Colonies slow-growing;
	   dark green to black,
	   felt-like aerial mycelium.

F. compacta	Extremely slow-growing.
F. dermatitidis	Black, yeastlike at first, gradually becoming filamentous at the periphery.

MICROSCOPIC

(On corn meal or Czapek's agar)

Phialophora ver-rucosa	*Phialophora* type of sporulation only, cup-shaped conidiophores with spores that bud from the base of the cup.
Cladosporium carionii	*Cladosporium* type of sporulation. only, tree-like branching conidiophores with conidia in abundance.
Fonsecaea pedrosoi *F. compacta* *F. dermatitidis*	3 types of sporulation, single or combined in one head: (a) *Cladosporium*, (b) *Phialophora*, and (c) pseudo-*Acrotheca*, conidia borne laterally on short protuberances on conidiophore. *F. compacta* differs from *F. pedrosoi* in its broad-based conidia; *F. dermatitidis*, in its yeast-like and *Pullularia* phases.

CHROMOBLASTOMYCOSIS

CHROMOBLASTOMYCOSIS, caused by several species of dematiaceous fungi, was defined by Dr. A. L. Carrión (1947) as a chronic, infectious, apparently non-contagious skin disease confined most frequently to one of the lower extremities and characterized clinically by the formation of nodular verrucous or tumor-like lesions. More recently, evidence of systemic disease has been reported. There are at least five species representing three genera which may cause this disease: *Phialophora verrucosa, Fonsecaea (Hormodendrum) pedrosoi, F. compacta, F. dermatitidis,* and *Cladosporium carrionii.*

Specimens for Examination

Crusts or exudates from the verrucous lesions may be submitted.

Cultural and Microscopic Characteristics

These fungi are dimorphic. In tissue, pus, or caseous material they are indistinguishable. They appear as large, round, yellowish-brown, thick-walled, often septate bodies. On Sabouraud's glucose medium they are filamentous at 22-25° and 37° C.

The colonies on this medium are slow-growing, dark green to black, felt-like in appearance with the exception of *F. dermatitidis,* and slightly embedded in the substrate. They cannot be differentiated by study of macroscopic characters alone, due to their striking cultural similarity. *F. dermatitidis* is at first yeast-like, gradually becoming mycelial at the periphery.

Species identification is based upon the method of sporulation, of which there are three types: *Phialophora,* characterized by cup-shaped conidiophores with spores which bud from the base of the cup; *Cladosporium,* by tree-like branching conidiophores

with conidia in chains; *Acrotheca*, by swollen conidiophores with lateral protuberances from which are borne, singly, ovoid condia. These three types of sporulation may occur simultaneously in a culture. *F. dermatitidis*, in addition to the three types of sporulation, also shows at a very early stage yeastlike and *Pullularia* phases.

P. verrucosa exhibits the *Phialophora* type of sporulation only.

F. pedrosoi, the most common incitant of chromoblastomycosis, possesses a triple sporulating ability. All three types of sporulation occur simultaneously and any one may predominate.

F. compacta exhibits the three types of sporulation, sometimes all combined in a single spore head with the *Cladosporium* type predominating.

F. dermatitidis exhibits early yeastlike and *Pullularia* phases, and later reveals, in addition, the three types of sporulation characteristic of the genus *Fonsecaea*.

C. carrionii shows the *Cladosporium* type of sporulation only. The pathogenic strains must be differentiated from saprophytic species of this genus on the basis of cultural characters. The pathogens grow at 22-25° and 37° C. and are slow growing, whereas the saprophytic forms are fast growing and do not grow at 37° C.

Pathogenicity for Animals

Rats and mice appear to be susceptible to these fungi injected by the intraperitoneal or intratesticular route.

Grateful acknowledgment is made to Dr. Margarita Silva for her assistance in the preparation of this section.

CHROMOBLASTOMYCOSIS

Figure 25

Histopathologic section from lesion in chromoblastomycosis, showing large septate bodies. X 800. (Courtesy of the late Dr. Rhoda Benham, Department of Dermatology, College of Physicians and Surgeons, Columbia University.)

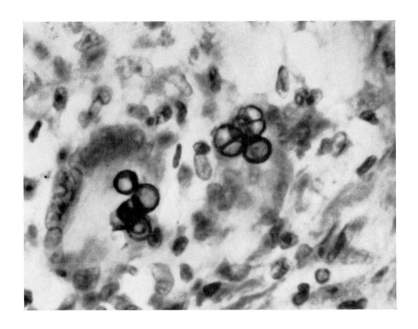

PHIALOPHORA VERRUCOSA
FONSECAEA PEDROSOI
FONSECAEA DERMATITIDIS

Figure 26

Phialophora verrucosa:

A. Colony on Sabouraud's glucose agar, four weeks.

B. Cup-shaped conidiophores with spores. X 400.

Fonsecaea pedrosoi:

C. Colony on Sabouraud's glucose agar, five weeks.

D-F. Three types of sporulation:

   D. *Cladosporium.* X 600.

   E. *Acrotheca.* X 600.

   F. *Phialophora.* X 600.

Fonsecaea dermatitidis:

G. Colony on Sabouraud's glucose agar, 25 days.

H. Yeastlike phase; note double budding cells. X 800.

I. *Pullularia* phase, showing clusters of spores along hyphae. X 200.

J. Same. X 800.

K. *Cladosporium* type of sporulation. X 800.

L. Same. X 600.

M. *Acrotheca* type of sporulation. X 800.

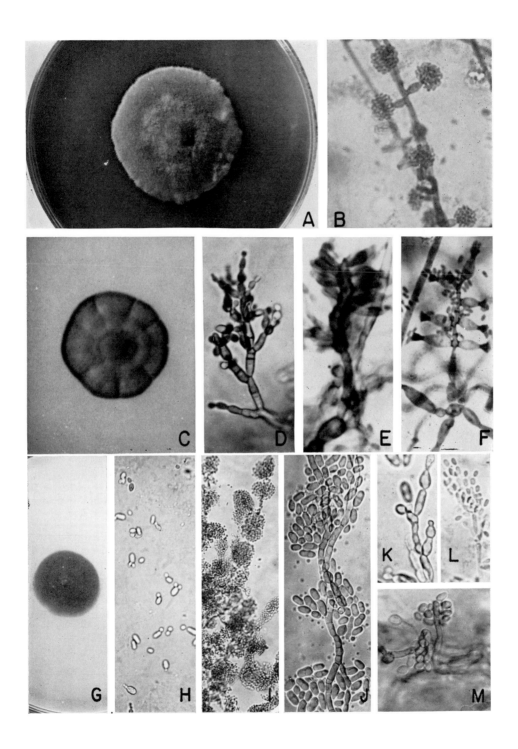

FONSECAEA COMPACTA
CLADOSPORIUM CARRIONII

Figure 27

Fonsecaea compacta:
    A. Colony on Sabouraud's glucose agar, six weeks.
    B. Complex conidial head. X 400.

Cladosporium carrionii:
    C. Colony on Sabouraud's glucose agar, four weeks.
    D. Cladosporium type of sporulation. X 400.

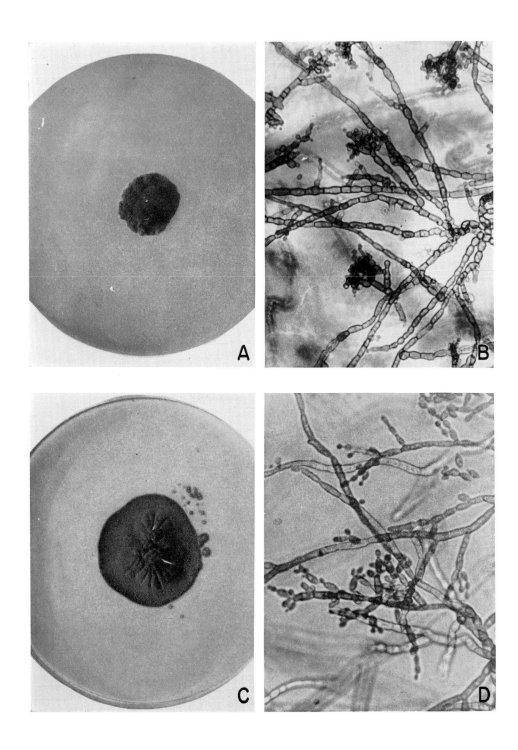

Contaminants

Saprophytic fungi are a constant nuisance in laboratories engaged in medical mycologic work. They appear frequently on the usual plating media, are often found in pathologic materials, and are at times mistaken for pathogenic fungi. To learn to differentiate between the saprophytic and the pathogenic fungi is a fundamental requirement in the laboratory attempting mycologic examinations if serious mistakes are to be avoided in the diagnosis of fungus disease.

Recognition of contaminants should not be difficult, provided one is familiar with a few of their common characteristics. The saprophytic fungi usually grow well at room temperature on the common mycologic media and poorly or not at all at 37° C.; they are, in general, highly pigmented, forming bluish-green or green, cream to yellow, orange, brown, deep rose, or black colonies, and nearly always produce an abundance of characteristic reproductive structures. The pathogenic fungi, on the other hand, are commonly slow-growing at room temperature or at 37° C. and often require special media for spore formation. There are some pathogenic fungi that form dark green or black pigments, and some species of contaminants that are white or light-colored. Therefore, a fungus isolated from a pathologic specimen should not be discarded as a saprophyte because of its pigment without a thorough cultural examination and microscopic study; neither should an isolate, because it is white, be considered a pathogen without an equally thorough study.

Eighteen common contaminants encountered in the laboratory are described and illustrated in the following pages. The giant colonies of all these fungi were grown on Sabouraud's glucose medium at room temperature. Classification by genus is adequate in the diagnostic laboratory for the identification of contaminants. Photomicrographs to illustrate the microscopic structural characteristics by which these contaminants can be identified generically are presented. These structures are best demonstrated in slide culture preparations on Czapek's or corn meal agar.

Penicillium sp.
Paecilomyces sp.

Figure 28

Penicillium sp.:

A. Colony fast-growing, attaining a diameter of 52 mm. in ten days; flat, with a powdery, bluish-green surface surrounded by a narrow white border.

B. Microscopically, the diagnostic structure known as the "penicillus" (a) or brush is seen. This structure consists of chains of spores pinched off from flask-shaped sterigmata (phialides) (b) borne in whorls from the ends of metulae (c) (short branches) arising from branched or unbranched conidiophores (d).

> Many species of this genus differ widely in color, texture, and rate of growth. Generic identification must be based upon demonstration of the "penicillus" or brush.

Paecilomyces sp.:

C. Colony rapidly-growing, attaining a diameter of 80 mm. in five days; flat with a surface of yellowish-brown, powdery mycelium.

D. Microscopically, the conidial-bearing structures (a) suggest *Penicillium* but differ in that the flask-shaped sterigmata (b) are long and tubular, bend away from the axis of the conidiophore (c) and are not always in verticils (whorls). Long well-separated chains of small elliptical conidia (d) are borne at the tips of the sterigmata.

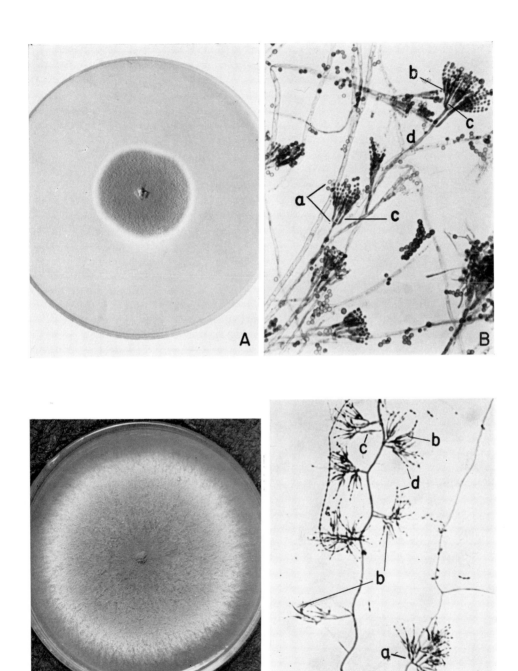

SCOPULARIOPSIS SP.
CEPHALOSPORIUM SP.

Figure 29

Scopulariopsis sp.:

A. Colony fast-growing, attaining a diameter of 65 mm. in eleven days; flat, at first white, later light-brown and powdery with a light-tan periphery; undersurface brownish at center, fading gradually to a light tan.

B. Microscopically, the hyphae bear many short, simple or branched conidiophores (a) which suggest the "penicillus" of *Penicillium*. The sterigmata (b) produce chains of lemon-shaped conidia (c) with a somewhat pointed apex and a truncate base. The mature spores are echinulate.

Cephalosporium sp.:

C. Colony moderately fast-growing, attaining a diameter of 51 mm. in seventeen days; compact, center slightly depressed, irregularly folded, cream-colored, felt-like, and surrounded by a slightly raised, pure white border of finely powdery mycelium, terminating in a thin long-napped mycelium; reverse, pale yellow.

D. Microscopically, numerous, elongate, hyaline conidia borne in spherical clusters (a) at the tips of long or short, lateral conidiophores (b).

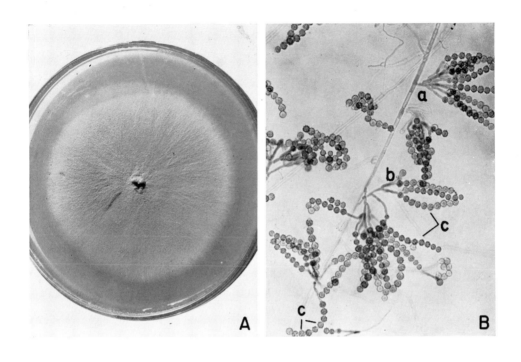

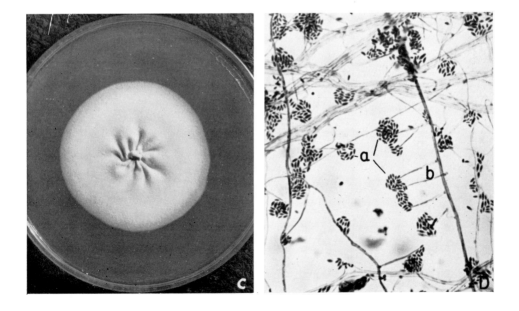

Trichosporon sp.
Rhodotorula sp.

Figure 30

Trichosporon sp.:

A. Colony moderately fast-growing, attaining a diameter of 40 mm. in thirteen days; ivory, membranous, and radially folded; center moist and yeastlike.

B. Microscopically, pseudomycelium and true mycelium are formed and many blastospores (a) and arthrospores (b).

> This fungus is often found as a contaminant in sputum. Formation of blastospores differentiates it from *Geotrichum*.

Rhodotorula sp.:

C. Colony slow-growing, attaining a diameter of 15 mm. in fourteen days; deep coral in color, low-convex, glistening, soft, and smooth, occasionally becoming wrinkled.

D. Microscopically, oval or round, thin-walled, budding cells.

> The genus consists of at least seven species showing a wide variation in shape and size of cell and in the number of buds (one to several) produced by a single cell, as well as in colony texture; they produce carotenoid pigments (red, orange or yellow). The cells form either no capsule or a faint one. No true mycelium or ascospores are produced.

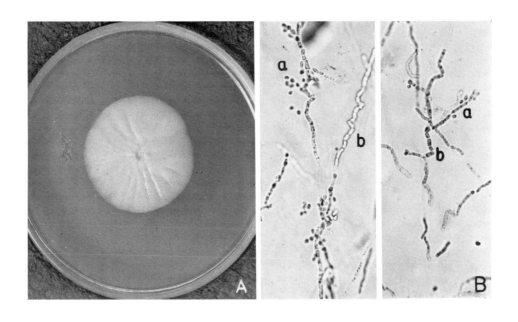

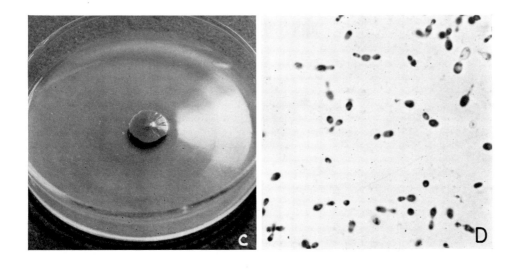

Monilia sitophila
Streptomyces sp.

Figure 31

Monilia sitophila:

A. Colony rapidly-growing, often completely filling the Petri plate or culture tube within three or four days; white at first, growing close to the surface of the agar, quickly becoming floccose and showing salmon-colored masses.

B. Microscopically, branching chains of ovate conidia (a) borne on short conidiophores (b); thick-walled arthrospores (c) formed by breaking up of the old hyphae into separate cells.

Streptomyces sp.:

C. Colony slow-growing, attaining a diameter of 8 mm. in eleven days; raised, slightly folded, hard, leathery, closely adherent to medium, and covered with a white aerial mycelium. Many species are variously pigmented, white, gray, red, rose, lavender, green, depending largely on the nature of the media and the conditions of growth. Characteristically they produce a strong musty odor.

D. Microscopically, long, branching aerial hyphae (a) of 1μ or less in diameter; from these hyphae arise spore-bearing filaments (sporophores) which, by segmentation, form chains of spherical or oval spores (b). The sporophores may be straight, wavy, loosely or tightly spiraled.

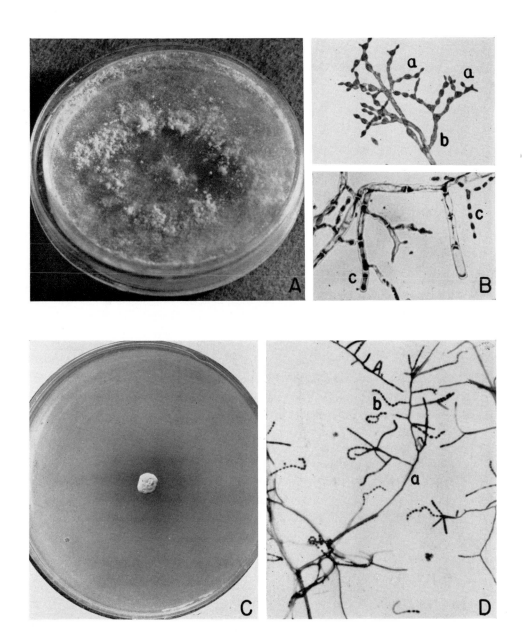

Fusarium sp.
Cladosporium (hormodendrum) sp.

Figure 32

Fusarium sp.:

A. Colony fast-growing, attaining a diameter of 55 mm. in seven days; at first white, later violet, with a center of heavy, fluffy mycelium, and a border of flat, white mycelium. This genus consists of many species, some of which are of different colors, white, tan, pink, violet, or red.

B. Microscopically, branched or unbranched conidiophores (a) on thin hyphae; the conidiophores produce two types of spores: macroconidia, long multi-septate, sickle-shaped (b); microconidia, ovoid, one-celled (c).

Cladosporium (Hormodendrum) sp.:

C. Colony moderately fast-growing, attaining a diameter of 42 mm. in seventeen days, irregularly heaped and folded, with a smooth, flat periphery; surface velvety, olive-green; undersurface, greenish-black. This fungus does not grow at 37° C., as do the pathogenic species of the same genus.

D. Microscopically, mycelium olivaceous; conidia in branching tree-like chains (a), borne from branched conidiophores (b) of variable lengths.

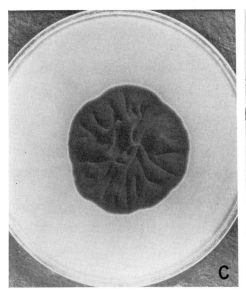

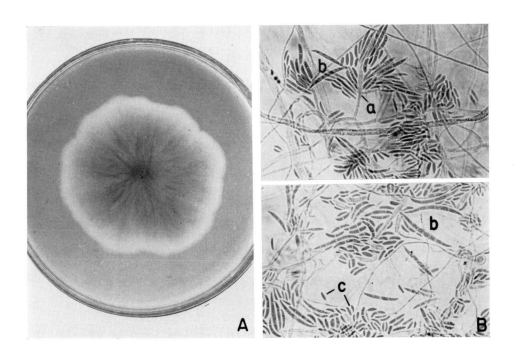

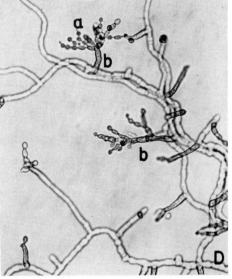

Phoma sp.
Pullularia sp.

Figure 33

Phoma sp.:

A. Colony fast-growing, attaining a diameter of 70 mm. in twelve days, consisting of two distinct zones, a central umbonated zone (35-40 mm.) of gray to taupe aerial mycelium and a peripheral zone (14 mm. wide) of shorter napped, brownish, aerial hyphae with concentric darker, shiny rings containing pycnidia; border flat, pinkish-tan, having an outermost layer of thin, cream to tan, submerged hyphae. Reverse shows a smudged brownish-black pigment at center with beige border.

B. Microscopically, the identifying structures are the globose or flask-shaped pycnidia (a); upon crushing, these are found to be filled with many, small, ovate to elongate, one-celled, hyaline pycnidiospores (b) that have been produced on short conidiophores inside the pycnidium. Some species of *Phoma* show pycnidia with one or more ostioles.

Pullularia sp.:

C. Colony fast-growing, attaining a diameter of 60 mm. in fourteen days; at first white, flat, and membranous, later showing an irregularly raised, folded, black shiny center of yeastlike appearance, surrounded by a flat, greenish-black border terminating in a fringe of greenish-white mycelium.

D. Microscopically, hyphae of two types: hyaline, thin-walled (a) when young, later dark and thick-walled (b); conidia elliptical, sometimes budding (c), borne by repetition at various fertile points on mycelium.

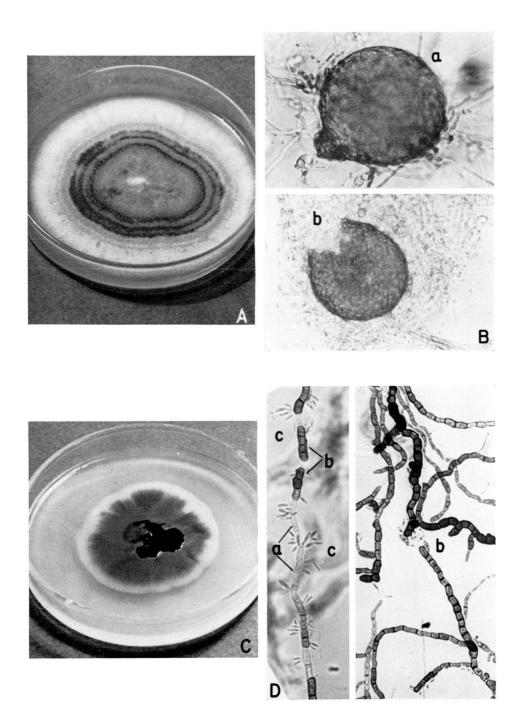

Helminthosporium sp.
Alternaria sp.

Figure 34

Helminthosporium sp.:

A. Colony moderately fast-growing, attaining a diameter of 40 mm. in fourteen days; grayish-green, raised, with surface of heavily matted, wooly mycelium.

B. Microscopically, hyphae light to dark, giving rise to long, septate, simple or branched conidiophores (a) having a knotted, twisted appearance; conidia brown, ovoid, containing four or more cells (b).

Alternaria sp.:

C. Colony rapidly growing, attaining a diameter of 75 mm. in nine days; grayish-white at first, later greenish-black; surface wooly or felt-like with loose, grayish mycelial tufts; border of grayish-white mycelium.

D. Microscopically, hyphae hyaline or dark; conidiophores (a) short or elongate, single or in groups, brown or greenish-brown; conidia (b) brown, transversely and longitudinally septate (muriform), borne singly or in acropetal chains.

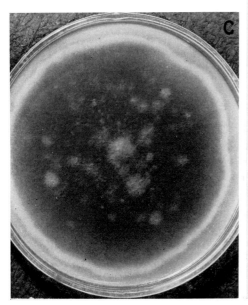

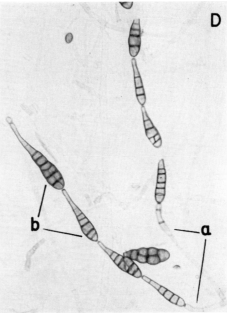

Aspergillus sp.
Syncephalastrum sp.

Figure 35

Aspergillus sp.:

A. Colony fast-growing, attaining a diameter of 70 mm. in seven days; flat, with a center of thin, grayish blue-green, somewhat floccose, matted mycelium, and border of sparse, partially submerged grayish mycelium; reverse, pale yellowish-green.

B. Microscopically, unbranched, nonseptate conidiophore (a) arising from a specialized cell (b) in the mycelium (foot-cell); at the apex of the conidiophore is the globose or elliptical vesicle (c) bearing phialides (d) (flask-shaped structures) from which are produced chains of conidia (e).

Syncephalastrum sp.:

C. Colony, rapidly-growing, quickly filling the Petri plate with a dense, white, fluffy, aerial mycelium, later dark gray.

D. Microscopically, mycelium nonseptate. Sporangiospores (a) borne serially within finger-like sporangioles (b) arising radially on inflated terminal ends (c) of branching sporangiophores (d).

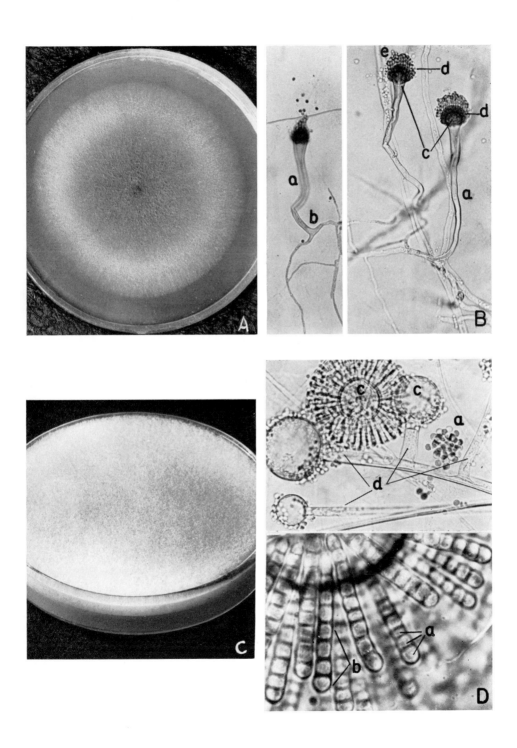

Mucor sp.
Rhizopus sp.

Figure 36

Mucor sp.:

A. Colony rapidly-growing, filling Petri dish with floccose aerial mycelium, first white, later gray.

B.-C. Microscopically, mycelium nonseptate; rhizoids absent; sporangiophores (a) branched or unbranched, borne at any point on the hyphae terminating in large, globose, many-spored sporangia (b); sporangial wall easily ruptured, scattering ellipsoid or globose spores (c), and revealing columella (d) (a swollen end of sporangiophore).

Rhizopus sp.:

D. Growth extremely rapid, cottony, grayish-white, aerial mycelium completely filling a Petri dish within three days.

E.-G. Microscopically, mycelium nonseptate. At the apex of a long, erect, unbranched sporangiophore (a) is borne the typical sporangium (b), a large spherical, black spore case filled with many round, brownish spores; sporangiophores arise singly or in small groups directly opposite rhizoids (c) (root-like structures) attached to the substrate and connected by hyphal branches (d) (stolons) running along the surface of the substrate. The ruptured sporangium, freed of spores, reveals columella (e).

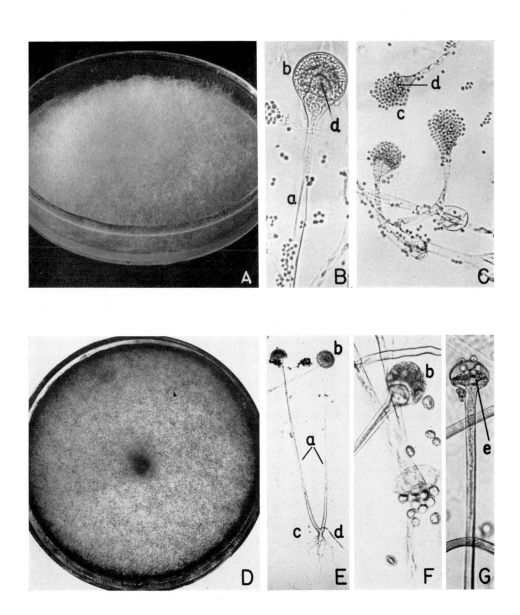

Media

Beef-Infusion Broth with Glucose *

Beef	450.0	gm.
Peptone (Difco proteose)	20.0	gm.
Sodium chloride	5.0	gm.
Glucose	10.0	gm.
Distilled water	1000.0	ml.

Beef-Infusion Agar with Glucose *

Beef	450.0	gm.
Distilled water	500.0	ml.

Agar	17.5	gm.
Peptone	10.0	gm.
Sodium chloride	5.0	gm.
Distilled water	500.0	ml.
Glucose	10.0	gm.

Beef-Heart Infusion Agar with Blood *

Beef heart	450.0	gm.
Distilled water	500.0	ml.

Agar	20.0	gm.
Sodium chloride	5.0	gm.
Peptone	10.0	gm.
Distilled water	500.0	ml.

Horse, sheep, or rabbit blood, defibrinated, sterile. . . . .50 ml. per 900 ml.

Beef-Infusion Agar with Blood and Antibiotics

Beef-heart infusion agar * or dehydrated blood agar base †. . . .	150.0	ml.

Horse blood, defibrinated, sterile.	10.0	ml.
Penicillin (50 units per ml. of medium).	8000.0	units
Streptomycin (50 units per ml. of medium).	8000.0	units

Glucose-Cystine-Veal Infusion Agar †

Veal infusion	1000.0	ml.
Peptone	10.0	gm.
NaCl	5.0	gm.
Agar	20.0	gm.
Cystine or cystine hydrochloride.	1.0	gm.

Glucose-Cystine-Veal Infusion Agar (cont.)

Glucose, 20% sterile solution	50.0 ml.
Blood (rabbit or horse)	80.0 ml.

Combine and heat at 60° for three hours.

Potato-Infusion Agar with Glucose ° †

Potatoes peeled and ground	200.0 gm.
Distilled water	1000.0 ml.
Agar	20.0 gm.
Glucose	20.0 gm.

Used unadjusted at pH 5.6-5.8 or adjusted subsequent to sterilization to pH 3.5 with a sterile 10% tartaric acid.

Corn Meal Agar °

Agar	17.50 gm.
Corn meal, yellow, ground	40.00 gm.
Distilled water	1000.00 ml.

Dissolve the agar in one-half the water by autoclaving. Add the corn meal to the remainder of the water and heat at approximately 65° for one hour. Filter through paper. Admix the dissolved agar and the corn meal filtrate (300-400 ml.) and filter through cotton. Dispense as required and autoclave twenty minutes. No pH adjustment is required.

Czapek's Agar

$NaNO_3$	2.00 gm.
K_2HPO_4	1.00 gm.
$MgSO_4 \cdot 7H_2O$	0.50 gm.
KCl	0.50 gm.
$FeSO_4$	0.01 gm.
Sucrose	30.00 gm.
Agar	15.00 gm.
Distilled water	1000.00 ml.

pH 6.6

Rice Medium °

Rice, white grains	7.0 gm.
Distilled water	28.0 ml.

Place rice and water in 300-ml. flasks; with rice grains evenly distributed over bottom of flask set evenly in the sterilizer and autoclave twenty minutes.

Sabouraud's Glucose Broth

Bacto-Peptone	10.0 gm.
Glucose	40.0 gm.
Distilled water to make	1000.0 ml.

Final pH 5.7.

Sabouraud's Glucose Agar * †

Agar	20.0 gm.
Peptone	10.0 gm.
Glucose, technical	40.0 gm.
Distilled water to make.	1000.0 ml.

Adjusted subsequent to sterilization to pH 5.6-5.8 with sterile 10% tartaric acid.

Sabouraud's Peptone Agar with Honey *

Agar	20.0 gm.
Peptone	10.0 gm.
Honey	60.0 gm.
Distilled water to make.	1000.0 ml.

Adjusted subsequent to sterilization to pH 5.6-5.8 with sterile 10% tartaric acid.

Carbohydrate Broth for Fermentation Tests with Candida

Difco beef extract.	3.0 gm.
Sodium chloride	5.0 gm.
Difco peptone	10.0 gm.
Distilled water	900.0 ml.

Heat to boiling and titrate exactly to pH 7.2. Add 100 ml. of indicator solution, filter, and dispense in 10-ml. quantities in Durham type fermentation tubes. Autoclave at 15 pounds pressure for exactly 15 minutes. Add 0.5 ml. of a 20-per-cent solution of the carbohydrate. The broth should not be kept for more than two or three weeks because slight changes in pH may occur.

Indicator solution

Brom-thymol-blue	0.04 gm.
Distilled water	100.00 ml.

Add a small amount of 1N NaOH to make the solution alkaline. When indicator is in solution, neutralize with 1N HCl until the exact neutral point is reached and one drop of either acid or alkali will cause a complete change of color.

(Martin, D. S., *et al.* J. Bact., 34:99, 1937)

Wort Agar * †

Agar	20.00	gm.
Ammonium chloride, NH₄Cl	1.00	gm.
Peptone	0.78	gm.
Maltose, technical	12.75	gm.
Malt extract	15.00	gm.
Dextrin	2.75	gm.
Glycerol	2.35	gm.
Dipotassium phosphate, K₂HPO₄	1.00	gm.
Distilled water	1000.00	ml.

* Formulae are based on those given in:
    Wadsworth, A. B.: Standard Methods of the Division of Laboratories and Research, New York State Department of Health, 3rd ed. Baltimore, Williams and Wilkins Co., 1947, chapter 13.
† The medium can be obtained commercially in the dehydrated form.

References

GENERAL

Mycologie Médicale. Communications et rapports présentés aux Journées de Mycologie Médicale (14-15 décembre 1956) organisées par l'Institut Pasteur et la Société Française de Mycologie Médicale. Paris, L'Expansion Scientifique Française. 344 p.

Ainsworth, G. C.: *Medical Mycology: An Introduction to its Problems.* New York, Pitman, 1952. 105 p.

Ajello, L.: Collecting specimens for the laboratory demonstration and isolation of fungi. *J. Amer. Med. Assoc., 146:*1581, 1951.

Ajello, L., Grant, V. Q., and Gutske, M. A.: The effect of tubercle concentration procedures on fungi causing pulmonary mycoses. *J. Lab. & Clin. Med., 38:* 486, 1951.

Alexopoulos, C. J.: *Introductory Mycology.* New York, Wiley, 1952, p. 312-338.

Ash, J. E., and Spitz, S.: *Pathology of Tropical Diseases: An Atlas.* Philadelphia, Saunders, 1945. 350 p.

Buell, C. B., and Weston, W. H.: Application of the mineral oil conservation method to maintaining collections of fungous cultures. *Amer. J. Botany, 34:* 555, 1947.

Cochrane, V. W.: *Physiology of Fungi.* New York, Wiley, 1958. 524 p.

Conant, N. F., *et al.: Manual of Clinical Mycology,* 2d ed. Philadelphia, Saunders, 1954. 456 p.

Cook, A. H., editor: *The Chemistry and Biology of Yeasts.* New York, Academic Press, 1958. 763 p.

Dodge, C. W.: *Medical Mycology: Fungous Diseases of Men and Other Mammals.* St. Louis, Mosby, 1935. 900 p.

Emmons, C. W.: Mycoses of animals. In Brandly, C. A., and Jungherr, E. L., editors: *Advances in Veterinary Science,* Vol. II. New York, Academic Press, 1955, p. 47-63.

Gordon, M. A.: A key to the human mycoses. *J. Bact., 63:*385, 1952.

Gridley, M. F.: A stain for fungi in tissue sections. *Amer. J. Clin. Path., 23:*303, 1953.

Grocott, R. G.: A stain for fungi in tissue sections and smears. Using Gomori's methenamine-silver-nitrate technic. *Amer. J. Clin. Path., 25:*975, 1955.

Hawker, L. E.: *The Physiology of Reproduction in Fungi.* Cambridge (England) Univ. Press, 1957. 128 p.

Jillson, O. F.: Mycology. *New England J. Med., 249:*523, 561, 1953.

Kenney, E. L.: *Practical Medical Mycology.* Springfield, Illinois, Thomas, 1955. 145 p.

Kligman, A. M., and DeLamater, E. D.: The immunology of the human mycoses. *Ann. Rev. Microbiol., 4:*283, 1950.

Kligman, A. M., Mescon, H., and DeLamater, E. D.: The Hotchkiss-McManus stain for the histopathologic diagnosis of fungus diseases. *Amer. J. Clin. Path., 21:*86, 1951.

Kurung, J. M.: The examination of sputum. I. Collection and selection. II. Search for elastic tissue. III. Search for fungal spores. *Amer. Rev. Tuberc.,* 76:671, 675, 679, 1957.

Lacaz, C. da Silva: *Manual de Micologia Médica,* 2d ed. São Paulo, Brazil, Irmãos Dupont, 1956. 422 p.

Langeron, M., and Vanbreuseghem, R.: *Précis de Mycologie,* 2d ed. Paris, Masson, 1952. 703 p.

Lewis, G. M., *et al.: An Introduction to Medical Mycology,* 4th ed. Chicago, Yr. Bk. Pub., 1958. 453 p.

Lodder, J., and Kreger-Van Rij, N. J. W.: *The Yeasts: A Taxonomic Study.* New York, Interscience, 1952. 713 p.

Moss, E. S., and McQuown, A. L.: *Atlas of Medical Mycology.* Baltimore, Williams & Wilkins, 1953. 245 p.

Nickerson, W. J.: Medical mycology. *Ann. Rev. Microbiol.,* 7:245, 1953.

Pelczar, M. J., Jr., and Reid, R. D.: *Microbiology.* New York, McGraw-Hill, 1958, p. 141-156.

Riddell, R. W.: Fungous diseases of Britain. *Brit. Med. J.,* 2:783, 1956.

Riddell, R. W.: Permanent stained mycological preparations obtained by slide culture. *Mycologia,* 42:265, 1950.

Skinner, C. E., Emmons, C. W., and Tsuchiya, H. M.: *Henrici's Molds, Yeasts and Actinomycetes,* 2d ed. New York, Wiley, 1947. 409 p.

Smith, D. T.: *Fungus Diseases of the Lungs.* Springfield, Illinois, Thomas, 1947, 59 p.

Smith, D. T.: Miscellaneous fungus diseases. *J. Chronic Dis.,* 5:528, 1957.

Wadsworth, A. B.: *Standard Methods of the Division of Laboratories and Research, New York State Department of Health,* 3rd ed. Baltimore, Williams & Wilkins, 1947, p. 466-478.

Weed, L. A.: Technics for the isolation of fungi from tissues obtained at operation and necropsy. *Amer. J. Clin. Path.,* 29:496, 1958.

Wilson, J. W.: *Clinical and Immunologic Aspects of Fungous Diseases.* Springfield, Illinois, Thomas, 1957. 280 p.

Zimmerman, L. E.: Fatal fungus infections complicating other diseases. *Amer. J. Clin. Path.,* 25:46, 1955.

DERMATOPHYTOSIS

Ajello, L.: The dermatophyte, *Microsporum gypseum,* as a saprophyte and parasite. *J. Invest. Dermat.,* 21:157, 1953.

Ajello, L., and Georg, L. K.: *In vitro* hair cultures for differentiating between atypical isolates of *Trichophyton mentagrophytes* and *Trichophyton rubrum.* Mycopath. et Mycol. Appl., 8:1, 1957.

Barlow, A. J. E., and Chattaway, F. W.: The parasitism of the ringworm group of fungi. *A.M.A. Arch. Dermat.,* 77:399, 1958.

Benedek, T.: Unilateral stimulation of *Microsporum audouini* by a new species of bacillus. *Mycologia,* 35:222, 1943.

Benham, R. W.: Effect of nutrition on growth and morphology of the dermatophytes. 1. Development of macroconidia in *Trichophyton rubrum. Mycologia,* 40:232, 1948.

Benham, R. W.: Nutritional studies of the dermatophyte—Effect on growth and morphology, with special reference to the production of marcroconidia. *Tr. New York Acad. Sci.*, 15:102, 1953.

Bocobo, F. C., and Benham, R. W.: Pigment production in the differentiation of *Trichophyton mentagrophytes* and *Trichophyton rubrum. Mycologia*, 41:291, 1949.

Conant, N. F.: Statistical analysis of spore size in genus *Microsporum. J. Invest. Dermat.*, 4:265, 1941.

Drouhet, E.: Recherches sur la nutrition des dermatophytes. II. Action des acides amines sur la croissance et la morphogenese. *Ann. Inst. Pasteur,* 82:348, 1952.

Drouhet, E.: Recherches sur la nutrition des dermatophytes. III. L'histidine, facteur de croissance des *Trichophyton* du groupe *rosaceum. Ann. Inst. Pasteur,* 85:791, 1953.

Drouhet, E., and Mariat, F.: Recherches sur la nutrition des dermatophytes. I. Étude des besoins vitaminiques. *Ann. Inst. Pasteur,* 82:338, 1952.

Emmons, C. W.: Dermatophytes; natural grouping based on the form of the spores and accessory organs. *Arch. Dermat. & Syph.,* 30:337, 1934.

Fowle, L. P., and Georg, L. K.: Suppurative ringworm contracted from cattle. *Arch. Dermat. & Syph.,* 56:780, 1947.

Georg, L. K.: The relation of nutrition to the growth and morphology of *Trichophyton faviforme. Mycologia,* 42:683, 1950.

Georg, L. K.: The relationship between the downy and granular forms of *Trichophyton mentagrophytes. J. Invest. Dermat.,* 23:123, 1954.

Georg, L. K.: *Trichophyton tonsurans* ringworm—A new public health problem. *Pub. Health Rep.,* 67:53, 1952.

Georg, L. K.: Use of a cycloheximide medium for isolation of dermatophytes from clinical materials. *A.M.A. Arch. Dermat. & Syph.,* 67:355, 1953.

Georg, L. K., and Camp, L. B.: Routine nutritional tests for the identifcation of dermatophytes. *J. Bact.,* 74:113, 1957.

Gordon, M. A.: The occurrence of the dermatophyte, *Microsporum gypseum,* as a saprophyte in soil. *J. Invest. Dermat.,* 20:201, 1953.

Hazen, E. L.: Effect of temperature and nutrition upon macroconidial formation of *Microsporum audouini. Mycologia,* 49:11, 1957.

Hazen, E. L.: *Microsporum audouini:* The effect of yeast extract, thiamine, pyridoxine and *Bacillus weidmaniensis* on the colony characteristics and macroconidial formation. *Mycologia,* 39:200, 1947.

Kligman, A. M.: Tinea capitis due to *M. audouini* and *M. canis.* II. Dynamics of the host-parasite relationship. *A.M.A. Arch. Dermat.,* 71:313, 1955.

Langeron, M., and Milochevitch, S.: Morphologie des dermatophytes sur milieux naturels et milieux à base de polysaccharides. Essai de classification. *Ann. Parasitol.,* 8:465, 1930.

Sabouraud, R.: *Maladies du Cuir Chevelu. III. Les Maladies Cryptogamiques. Les Teignes.* Paris, Masson, 1910. 855 p.

Silva, M.: Nutritional studies of the dermatophytes—Factors affecting pigment production. *Tr. New York Acad. Sci.,* 15:106, 1953.

Silva, M., and Benham, R. W.: Nutritional studies of the dermatophytes with special reference to the red-pigment-producing varieties of *Trichophyton mentagrophytes. J. Invest. Dermat.,* 22:285, 1954.

Silva, M., Kesten, B. M., and Benham, R. W.: *Trichophyton rubrum* infections: A clinical, mycologic and experimental study. *J. Invest. Dermat.,* 25:311, 1955.

Actinomycosis

Emmons, C. W.: *Actinomyces* and actinomycosis. *Puerto Rico J. Pub. Health & Trop. Med.,* 11:63, 1935.

Emmons, C. W.: The isolation of *Actinomyces bovis* from tonsillar granules. *Pub. Health Rep.,* 53:1967, 1938.

Erikson, D.: *Pathogenic Anaerobic Organisms of the Actinomyces Group.* London, His Majesty's Stat. Off., 1940, 63 pp.

Erickson, D., and Porteous, J. W.: Commensalism in pathogenic anaerobic *Actinomyces* cultures. *J. Gen. Microbiol.,* 13:261, 1955.

Hazen, E. L., and Little, G. N.: *Actinomyces bovis* and "anaerobic diphtheroids": Pathogenicity for hamsters and other differentiating characteristics. *J. Lab. & Clin. Med.,* 51:968, 1958.

King, S., and Meyer, E.: Metabolic and serologic differentiation of *Actinomyces bovis* and "anaerobic diphtheroids." *J. Bact.,* 74:234, 1957.

Meyer, E., and Verges, P.: Mouse pathogenicity as a diagnostic aid in the identification of *Actinomyces bovis. J. Lab. & Clin. Med.,* 36:667, 1950.

Negroni, P., and Bonfiglioli, H.: Morphology and biology of *Actinomyces israeli* (Kruse). *J. Trop. Med. & Hyg.,* 40:226, 240, 1937.

Peabody, J. W., and Seabury, J. H.: Actinomycosis and nocardiosis. *J. Chron. Dis.,* 5:374, 1957.

Rosebury, T., Epps, L. J., and Clark, A.: A study of the isolation, cultivation and pathogenicity of *Actinomyces israeli* recovered from the human mouth and from actinomycosis in man. *J. Infect. Dis.,* 74:131, 1944.

Suter, L. S.: Evaluation of criteria used in the identification of *Actinomyces bovis* with particular reference to the catalase reaction. *Mycopath. et Mycol. Appl.,* 7:220, 1956.

Thompson, L.: Isolation and comparison of *Actinomyces* from human and bovine infections. *Proc. Staff Meet., Mayo Clinic,* 25:81, 1950.

Weed, L. A., and Baggenstoss, A. H.: Actinomycosis. A pathologic and bacteriologic study of twenty-one fatal cases. *Amer. J. Clin. Path.,* 19:201, 1949.

Wilson, G. S., and Miles, A. A.: *Topley and Wilson's Principles of Bacteriology and Immunity,* 4th ed., Vol. 1. Baltimore, Williams & Wilkins, 1955, p. 457-478.

Wright, J. H.: The biology of the microorganism of actinomycosis. *J. Med. Research,* 13:349, 1905.

Nocardiosis

Conant, N. F.: Medical Mycology. *Nocardia* (Aerobic Actinomycetes): In Dubos, R. J.: *Bacterial and Mycotic Infections of Man,* 3rd ed. Philadelphia, Lippincott, 1958. p. 584-589.

González Ochoa, A.: Estudio comparativo entre *Actinomyces mexicanus, A. brasiliensis* y *A. asteroides. Rev. Inst. Salub. y Enferm. Trop.,* 6:155, 1945.

González Ochoa, A., and Sandoval, M. A.: Características de las actinomicetes pathogenos más comunes. *Rev. Inst. Salub. y Enferm. Trop.,* 16:149, 1955.

Gordon, R. E., and Smith, M. M.: Proposed group of characters for the separation of *Streptomyces* and *Nocardia. J. Bact.,* 69:147, 1955.

Mackinnon, J. E., and Artagaveytia-Allende, R. C.: The main species of pathogenic aerobic actinomycetes causing mycetomas. *Tr. Roy. Soc. Trop. Med. & Hyg.,* 50:31, 1956.

Mariat, F.: Physiologie des actinomycetes aerobies pathogenes. *Mycopath. et Mycol. Appl.,* 9:111, 1958.

Waksman, S. A.: *The Actinomycetes: Their Nature, Occurrence, Activities, and Importance.* Waltham, Mass., Chronica Botanica Co., 1950. 230 p.

Wilson, G. S., and Miles, A. A.: *Topley and Wilson's Principles of Bacteriology and Immunity,* 4th ed., Vol. 1. Baltimore, Williams & Wilkins, 1955, p. 457-478.

BLASTOMYCOSIS

Curtis, A. C., and Bocobo, F. C.: North American blastomycosis. *J. Chronic Dis.,* 5:404, 1957.

Halliday, W. J., and McCoy, E.: Biotin as a growth requirement for *Blastomyces dermatitidis. J. Bact.,* 70:464, 1955.

Layton, J. M., McKee, A. P., and Stamler, F. W.: Dual infection with *Blastomyces dermatitidis* and *Histoplasma capsulatum. Amer. J. Clin. Path.,* 23:904, 1953.

Manwaring, J. H.: Unusual forms of *Blastomyces dermatitidis* in human tissues. *Arch. Path.,* 48:421, 1949.

Nickerson, W. J.: Physiological bases of morphogenesis in animal disease fungi. *Tr. New York Acad. Sci.,* 13:140, 1951.

Salvin, S. B.: Phase-determining factors in *Blastomyces dermatitidis. Mycologia,* 41:311, 1949.

Schwarz, J., and Baum, G. L.: Blastomycosis. *Amer. J. Clin. Path.,* 21:999, 1951.

Smith, J. G., Jr., Harris, J. S., Conant, N. F., and Smith, D. T.: An epidemic of North American blastomycosis. *J. Amer. Med. Assoc.,* 158:641, 1955.

Tompkins, V., and Schleifstein, J.: Small forms of *Blastomyces dermatitidis* in human tissues. *A.M.A. Arch. Path.,* 55:432, 1953.

Weed, L. A.: North American blastomycosis. *Amer. J. Clin. Path,* 25:37, 1955.

SOUTH AMERICAN BLASTOMYCOSIS

Almeida, F. de: Formas pequeñas de *P. brasiliensis, B. dermatitidis* e *H. capsulatum* nos tecidos. *An. Fac. Med. Univ. S. Paulo,* 28:141, 1954.

Fonseca, J. B.: Blastomicose Sul-Americana. Estudo das lesões dentárias e paradentárias sob o ponto de vista clínico e histopathológico. Tese apresentada à Faculdade de Farmácia e Odontologia da Universidade de São Paulo. *São Paulo, Gráfico Politipo Ltdr.,* 1957. 182 p.

Furtado, T. A., Wilson, J. W., and Plunkett, O. A.: South American blastomycosis or paracoccidioidomycosis. The mycosis of Lutz, Splendore, and Almeida. *A.M.A. Arch. Dermat. & Syph.,* 70:166, 1954.

Lacaz, C. da Silva: South American blastomycosis. *An. Fac. Med. Univ. S. Paulo,* 29:1, 1955-56.

Perry, H. O., Weed, L.A., and Kierland, R. R.: South American blastomycosis. Report of case and review of laboratory features. *A.M.A. Arch. Dermat. & Syph.,* 70:477, 1954.

Moniliasis

Ajello, L. A.: A simple method for preparing corn meal agar. *Mycologia, 37:* 636, 1945.

Benham, R. W.: Species of *Candida* most frequently isolated from man: Methods and criteria for their identification. *J. Chron. Dis., 5:*460, 1957.

Drouhet, E., and Vieu, M.: Facteurs vitaminiques de croissance des *Candida. Ann. Inst. Pasteur, 92:*825, 1957.

Gordon, M. A.: Differentiation of yeasts by means of fluorescent antibody. *Proc. Soc. Exper. Biol. & Med., 97:*694, 1958.

Gordon, M. A., Bradley, E. G., and Grant, V. Q.: The influence of different types of corn meal agar upon chlamydospore production of *Candida albicans. J. Lab. & Clin. Med., 40:*316, 1952.

Kligman, A. M.: Aids in technic in the identification of *Candida albicans. J. Invest. Dermat., 14:*173, 1950.

Nickerson, W. J., and Mankowski, Z.: A polysaccharide medium of known composition favoring chlamydospore formation in *Candida albicans. J. Infect. Dis., 92:*20, 1953.

Pollack, J. D., and Benham, R. W.: The chlamydospores of *Candida albicans:* Comparison of three media for their induction. *J. Lab. & Clin. Med., 50:*313, 1957.

Reid, J. D., Jones, M. M., and Carter, E. B.: A simple clear medium for demonstration of chlamydospores of *Candida albicans. Amer. J. Clin. Path., 23:*938, 1953.

Skinner, C. E.: The yeast-like fungi: *Candida* and *Brettanomyces. Bact. Rev., 11:*227, 1947.

Taschdjian, C. L.: Routine identification of *Candida albicans:* Current methods and a new medium. *Mycologia, 49:*332, 1957.

Wickerham, L. J.: Apparent increase in frequency of infections involving *Torulopsis glabrata.* Procedure for its identification. *J. Amer. Med. Assoc., 165:*47, 1957.

Coccidioidomycosis

Creitz, J. R., and Puckett, T. F.: A method for cultural identification of *Coccidioides immitis. Amer. J. Clin. Path., 24:*1318, 1954.

Emmons, C. W.: Biology of Coccidioides. In Nickerson, W. J.: *Biology of Pathogenic Fungi.* Waltham, Mass., Chronica Botanica Co., 1947, p. 71-82.

Fiese, M. J.: Coccidioidomycosis. Springfield, Illinois, Thomas, 1958. 253 p.

Friedman, L., and Pappagianis, D.: The inhibitory effect of peptone on the sporulation of three strains of *Coccidioides immitis. Amer. Rev. Tuberc., 74:* 147, 1956.

Friedman, L., Pappagianis, D., Berman, R. J., and Smith, C. E.: Studies on *Coccidioides immitis:* Morphology and sporulation capacity of forty-seven strains. *J. Lab. & Clin. Med., 42:*438, 1953.

Friedman, L., Smith, C. E., Roessler, W. G., and Berman, R. J.: The virulence and infectivity of twenty-seven strains of *Coccidioides immitis. Amer. J. Hyg., 64:*198, 1956.

Georg, L. K., Ajello, L., and Gordon, M. A.: A selective medium for the isolation of *Coccidioides immitis*. *Science, 114*:387, 1951.

Huppert, M., and Walker, L. J.: The selective and differential effects of cycloheximide on many strains of *Coccidioides immitis*. *Amer. J. Clin. Path., 29*:291, 1958.

Smith, D. T., and Harrell, E. R., Jr.: Fatal coccidioidomycosis. A case of a laboratory infection. *Amer. Rev. Tuberc., 57*:368, 1948.

United States Public Health Service, Communicable Disease Center: Proceedings of Symposium on Coccidioidomycosis, Phoenix, Arizona, February 11-13, 1957. Washington, D.C., *Public Health Service Publication No. 575, 1957.* 197 p.

CRYPTOCOCCOSIS

Benham, R. W.: Cryptococcosis and blastomycosis. *Ann. New York Acad. Sci., 50*:1299, 1950.

Benham, R. W.: The genus *Cryptococcus*. *Bact. Rev., 20*:189, 1956.

Cox, L. B., and Tolhurst, J. C.: *Human Torulosis. A Clinical, Pathological and Microbiological Study, with a Report of Thirteen Cases.* Melbourne, Australia, Melbourne Univ. Press, 1946. 149 p.

Drouhet, E., Ségrétain, G., and Aubert, J.-P.: Polyoside capsulaire d'un champignon pathogene, *Torulopsis neoformans*. Relation avec la virulence. *Ann. Inst. Pasteur, 79*:891, 1950.

Emmons, C. W.: *Cryptococcus neoformans* strains from a severe outbreak of bovine mastitis. *Mycopath. et Mycol. Appl., 6*:231, 1952.

Emmons, C. W.: Saprophytic sources of *Cryptococcus neoformans* associated with the pigeon (*Columba livia*). *Amer. J. Hyg., 62*:227, 1955.

Evans, E. E., and Harrell, E. R., Jr.: Cryptococcosis (Torulosis); A review of recent cases. *Univ. Michigan Med. Bull., 18*:43, 1952.

Kao, C. J., and Schwarz, J.: The isolation of *Cryptococcus neoformans* from pigeon nests. With remarks on the identification of virulent cryptococci. *Amer. J. Clin. Path., 27*:652, 1957.

Littman, M. L.: Capsule synthesis by *Cryptococcus neoformans*. *Tr. New York Acad. Sci., 20*:623, 1958.

Littman, M. L.: An improved method for detection of urea hydrolysis by fungi. *J. Infect. Dis., 101*:51, 1957.

Littman, M. L., and Zimmerman, L. E.: *Cryptococcosis: Torulosis or European Blastomycosis.* New York, Grune & Stratton, 1956. 205 p.

Seeliger, H. P. R.: Use of a urease test for the screening and identification of cryptococci. *J. Bact., 72*:127, 1956.

Wilson, J. W.: Cryptococcosis (Torulosis, European blastomycosis, Busse-Buschke's disease). *J. Chronic Dis., 5*:445, 1957.

GEOTRICHOSIS

Bendove, R. A., and Ashe, B. I.: *Geotrichum* septicemia. Report of a case. *A.M.A. Arch. Int. Med., 89*:107, 1952.

Carmichael, J. W.: *Geotrichum candidum. Mycologia, 49:*820, 1957.

Kaliski, S. R., Beene, M. L., and Mattman, L.: *Geotrichum* in blood stream of an infant. *J. Amer. Med. Assoc., 148:*1207, 1952.

Kunstadter, R. H., Milzer, A., and Whitcomb, F.: Bronchopulmonary geotrichosis in children. *Amer. J. Dis. Child., 79:*82, 1950.

Minton, R., Young, R. V., and Shanbrom, E.: Endobronchial geotrichosis. *Ann. Int. Med., 40:*340, 1954.

Smith, D. T.: *Fungus Diseases of the Lungs.* Springfield, Illinois, Thomas, 1947, p. 16-19.

Thjötta, Th., and Urdal, K.: A family endemic of geotrichosis pulmonum. *Acta Path. et Microbiol. Scand., 26:*673, 1949.

Webster, B. H.: Pulmonary geotrichosis. *Amer. Rev. Tuberc., 76:*286, 1957.

Histoplasmosis

Proceedings of the Histoplasmosis Seminar, Cincinnati, Ohio, Feb. 11, 1958, sponsored by the Jewish Hospital Association, Cincinnati. Published by the Association (mimeo.), 1958. 100 p.

Ajello, L.: Geographic distribution of *Histoplasma capsulatum. Mykosen, 1:*147, 1958.

Binford, C. H.: Histoplasmosis. Tissue reactions and morphologic variations of the fungus. *Amer. J. Clin. Path., 25:*25, 1955.

Campbell, C. C.: Reverting *Histoplasma capsulatum* to the yeast phase. *J. Bact., 54:*263, 1947.

Conant, N. F.: A cultural study of the life cycle of *Histoplasma capsulatum* Darling 1906. *J. Bact., 41:*563, 1941.

Drouhet, E.: Quelques aspects biologiques et mycologiques de l'histoplasmose. *Semaine des Hopitaux, Paris, 33:*1299, 1957.

Drouhet, E., and Schwarz, J.: Croissance et morphogénese d'*Histoplasma.* 1. Étude comparative des phases mycélienne et levure de 18 souches d'*Histoplasma capsulatum* d'origine Américaine et Africaine. *Ann. Inst. Pasteur, 90:*144, 1956.

Duncan, J. T.: Tropical African histoplasmosis. *Tr. Royal Soc. Trop. Med. & Hyg., 52:*468, 1958.

Edwards, G. A., Edwards, M. R., and Hazen, E. L.: Electron microscopic study of *Histoplasma* in mouse spleen. *J. Bact., 17:*429, 1959.

Edwards, M. R., Hazen, E. L., and Edwards, G. A.: The fine structure of the yeastlike cells of *Histoplasma* in culture. *J. Gen. Microbiol., 20:*496, 1959.

Emmons, C. W.: The significance of saprophytism in the epidemiology of the mycoses. *Tr. New York Acad. Sci., 17:*157, 1954.

Furcolow, M. L.: Recent studies on the epidemiology of histoplasmosis. *Ann. New York Acad. Sci., 72:*127, 1958.

Howell, A.: The efficiency of methods for the isolation of *Histoplasma capsulatum. Pub. Health Rep., 63:*173, 1948.

Kurung, J. M.: The isolation of *Histoplasma capsulatum* from sputum. *Am. Rev. Tuberc., 66:*578, 1952.

Littman, M. L.: Liver-spleen glucose blood agar for *Histoplasma capsulatum* and other fungi. *Amer. J. Clin. Path., 25:*1148, 1955.

Lopez Fernandez, J. R.: Acción pathógena experimental de la levadura *Torulopsis glabrata* (Anderson 1917) lodder y de vries, 1938 productora de lesiones histopathológicas semejantes a las de la histoplasmosis. *An. Fac. Med.,* Montevìdeo, *37:*470, 1952.

Pine, L., and Peacock, C. L.: Studies on the growth of *Histoplasma capsulatum.* IV. Factors influencing conversion of the mycelial phase to the yeast phase. *J. Bact., 75:*167, 1958.

Salvin, S. B.: Cysteine and related compounds in the growth of the yeastlike phase of *Histoplasma capsulatum. J. Infect. Dis., 84:*275, 1949.

Scherr, G. H.: Studies on the dimorphism of *Histoplasma capsulatum.* 1. The roles of -SH groups and incubation temperature. *Exper. Cell Res., 12:*92, 1957.

United States Public Health Service. *Proceedings of the Conference on Histoplasmosis,* Excelsior Springs, Missouri, Nov. 18-20, 1952. Washington, D.C., Gov. Printing Office, (Pub. Health Monograph No. 39), 1956. 322 p.

Vanbreuseghem, R: *Histoplasma duboisii* and large forms of *Histoplasma capsulatum. Mycologia, 48:*264, 1956.

Weed, L. A., and Parkhill, E. M.: The diagnosis of histoplasmosis in ulcerative disease of the mouth and pharynx. *Am. J. Clin. Path., 18:*130, 1948.

Aspergillosis

Enjalbert, L., Ségrétain, G., Eschapasse, H., Moreau, G., and Bourdin, M.: Deux cas d'aspergillose pulmonaire. Etude anatomo-pathologique. *Semaine des Hôpitaux, Paris, 33:*1, 1957.

Hinson, K. F. W., Moon, A. J., and Plummer, N. S.: Broncho-pulmonary aspergillosis; a review and a report of eight new cases. *Thorax, 7:*317, 1952.

Kirschstein, R. L., and Sidransky, H.: Mycotic endocarditis of the tricuspid valve due to *Aspergillus flavus. A.M.A. Arch. Path., 62:*103, 1956.

Ségrétain, G., and Vieu, M.: Formes parasitaires des Aspergillus dans l'aspergillome bronchique: Diagnostic biologique des aspergilloses broncho-pulmonaires. *Semaine des Hôpitaux, Paris, 33:*1281, 1957.

Stuart, E. A., and Blank, F.: Aspergillosis of the ear. A report of twenty-nine cases. *Can. Med. Assoc. J., 72:*334, 1955.

Thom, C., and Raper, K. B.: *A Manual of the Aspergilli.* Baltimore, Williams and Wilkins, 1945. 373 p.

Vellios, F., Crawford, A. S., Gatzimos, C. D., and Haynes, E.: Bronchial aspergillosis occurring as an intracavitary "fungus ball." *Amer. J. Clin. Path., 27:* 68, 1957.

Ziskind, J., Pizzolato, P., and Buff, E. E.: Aspergillosis of the brain. Report of a case. *Amer. J. Clin. Path., 29:*554, 1958.

Mucormycosis

Baker, R. D.: The diagnosis of fungus diseases by biopsy. *J. Chronic Dis., 5:* 552, 1957.

Baker, R. D.: Mucormycosis. A new disease? *J. Amer. Med. Assoc., 163:*805, 1957.

Baker, R. D.: Pulmonary mucormycosis. *Amer. J. Path., 32:*287, 1956.

Bauer, H., Ajello, L., Adams, E., and Hernandez, D. U.: Cerebral mucormycosis: Pathogensis of the disease. *Amer. J. Med., 18:*822, 1955.

Gregory, J. E., Golden, A., and Haymaker, W.: Mucormycosis of the central nervous system. A report of three cases. *Bull. Johns Hopkins Hosp., 73:*405, 1943.

Kurrein, F.: Cerebral mucormycosis. *J. Clin. Path., 7:*141, 1954.

MADUROMYCOSIS

Ajello, L.: The isolation of *Allescheria boydii* Shear, an etiologic agent of mycetomas, from soil. *Amer. J. Trop. Med. & Hyg., 1:*227, 1952.

Benham, R. W., and Georg, L. K.: *Allescheria boydii,* causative agent in a case of meningitis. *J. Invest. Dermat., 10:*99, 1948.

Burns, E. L., Moss, E. S., and Brueck, J. W.: Mycetoma pedis in the United States and Canada. With a report of three cases originating in Louisiana. *Amer. J. Clin. Path., 15:*35, 1945.

Emmons, C. W.: *Allescheria boydii* and *Monosporium apiospermum. Mycologia, 36:*188, 1944.

Mackinnon, J. E.: A contribution to the study of the causal organisms of maduromycosis. *Tr. Roy. Soc. Trop. Med. & Hyg., 48:*470, 1954.

Mackinnon, J. E., Ferrada-Urgua, L. V., and Montemayor, L.: *Madurella grisea* n sp. A new species of fungus producing the black variety of maduromycosis in South America. *Mycopathologia, 4:*384, 1949.

Nauhauser, I.: Black grain maduromycosis caused by *Madurella grisea.* Report of the first North American case and its response to therapy with diaminodiphenylsulfone. *A.M.A. Arch. Dermat., 72:*550, 1955.

Ségrétain, G.: Diagnostic biologique des maduromycoses. *Semaine des Hôpitaux, Paris, 33:*951, 1957.

SPOROTRICHOSIS

Arthur, G. W., and Albrittain, J. W.: Disseminated cutaneous sporotrichosis with systemic involvement. *A.M.A. Arch. Dermat., 77:*187, 1958.

Benham, R. W., and Kesten, B.: Sporotrichosis; its transmission to plants and animals. *J. Infect. Dis., 50:*437, 1932.

Campbell, C. C.: Use of Francis' glucose cystine blood agar in the isolation and cultivation of *Sporotrichum schenckii. J. Bact., 50:*233, 1945.

Gastineau, F. M., Spolyar, L. W., and Haynes, E.: Sporotrichosis; report of six cases among florists. *J. Amer. Med. Assoc., 117:*1074, 1941.

Hopkins, J. G., and Benham, R. W.: Sporotrichosis in New York State. *New York State J. Med., 32:*595, 1932.

Mikkelsen, W. M., Brandt, R. L., and Harrell, E. R.: Sporotrichosis: A report of 12 cases, including two with skeletal involvement. *Ann. Int. Med., 47:*435, 1957.

Shoemaker, E. H., *et al.:* Leptomeningitis due to *Sporotrichum schenckii. A.M.A. Arch. Path., 64:*222, 1957.

Union of South Africa Transvaal Mine Medical Officers' Association: *Sporotri-chosis Infection on Mines of the Witwatersrand: A Symposium.* Johannesburg, S. Africa, Transvaal Chamber of Mines, 1947. 67 p.

CHROMOBLASTOMYCOSIS

Binford, C. H., Hess, G., and Emmons, C. W.: Chromoblastomycosis: Report of a case from continental United States and discussion of the classification of the causative fungus. *Arch. Dermat. & Syph., 49:* 398, 1944.

Binford, C. H., Thompson, R. K., and Gorham, M. E.: Mycotic brain abscess due to *Cladosporium trichoides,* a new species. *Amer. J. Clin. Path., 22:*535, 1952.

Brumpt, E.: *Précis de Parasitologie,* 3rd ed. Paris, Masson, 1922. 679 p.

Carrión, A. L.: Chromoblastomycosis. *Ann. New York Acad. Sci., 50:*1255, 1950.

Carrión, A. L.: Yeastlike dematiaceous fungi infecting the human skin. Special reference to so-called *Hormiscium dermatitidis. Arch. Dermat. & Syph., 61:* 996, 1950.

Carrión, A. L., and Silva, M.: Chromoblastomycosis and its Etiologic Fungi. In Nickerson, W. J.: *Biology of Pathogenic Fungi.* Waltham, Mass., Chronica Botanica Co., 1947, 20-64 p.

Conant, N. F.: The occurrence of a human pathogenic fungus as a saprophyte in nature. *Mycologia,* 29:597, 1937.

King, A. B., and Collette, T. S.: Brain abscess due to *Cladosporium trichoides:* Report of the second case due to this organism. *Bull. Johns Hopkins Hosp., 91:*298, 1952.

Martin, D. S., Baker, R. D., and Conant, N. F.: A case of verrucous dermatitis caused by *Hormodendrum pedrosoi* (chromoblastomycosis) in North Carolina. *Amer. J. Trop. Med.,* 16:593, 1936.

McGill, H. C., Jr., and Brueck, J. W.: Brain abscess due to *Hormodendrum* species. Report of third case. *A.M.A. Arch. Path.,* 62:303, 1956.

Medlar, E. M.: A new fungus, *Phialophora verrucosa,* pathogenic for man. *Mycologia,* 7:200, 1915.

Ségrétain, G., Mariat, F. and Drouhet, E.: Sur *Cladosporium trichoides* isolé d'une mycose cérébrale. *Ann. Inst. Pasteur,* 89:465, 1955.

Silva, M.: The parasitic phase of the fungi of chromoblastomycosis: Develop-ment of sclerotic cells *in vitro* and *in vivo. Mycologia,* 49:318, 1957.

Silva, M.: The saprophytic phase of the fungi of chromoblastomycosis: Effect of nutrients and temperature upon growth and morphology. *Tr. New York Acad. Sci.,* 21:46, 1958.

Simson, F. W., Harington, C., and Barnetson, J.: Chromoblastomycosis: A report of six cases. *J. Path. & Bact.,* 55:191, 1943.

Trejos, A.: *Cladosporium carrionii* n. sp. and the problem of *Cladosporia* isolated from chromoblastomycosis. *Rev. Biol. Trop.* 2(1):75, 1954.

CONTAMINANTS

Barnett, H. L.: *Illustrated Genera of Imperfect Fungi.* Minneapolis, Burgess, 1955. 218 p.

Conant, N. F., *et al.*: *Manual of Clinical Mycology*, 2nd ed. Philadelphia, Saunders, 1954, p. 390-411.

Gilman, J. C.: *A Manual of Soil Fungi*, 2nd ed. Ames, Iowa State College Press, 1957. 450 p.

Lewis, G. M., *et al.*: *An Introduction to Medical Mycology*, 4th ed., Chicago, Yr. Bk. Pub., 1958, p. 423-440.

Lodder, J., and Kreger-Van Riji, N. J. W.: *The Yeasts. A Taxonomic Study*. New York, Interscience, 1952. 713 p.

Raper, K. B., Thom, C., and Fennel, D. I.: *A Manual of the* Penicillia. Baltimore, Williams and Wilkins, 1949. 875 p.

Thom, C., and Raper, K. B.: *A Manual of the* Aspergilli. Baltimore, Williams and Wilkins, 1945. 373 p.